American Country Christmas

1992

COMPILED & EDITED BY
PATRICIA DREAME WILSON
& BRENDA WALDRON KOLB

Oxmoor
House®

©1992 by Oxmoor House, Inc.
Book Division of Southern Progress Corporation
P.O. Box 2463, Birmingham, Alabama 35201

Library of Congress Catalog Number: 89-61909
ISBN: 0-8487-1093-2
ISSN: 1044-4904
Manufactured in the United States of America
First Printing

Editor-in-Chief: Nancy J. Fitzpatrick
Senior Homes Editor: Mary Kay Culpepper
Senior Editor, Editorial Services: Olivia Kindig Wells
Director of Manufacturing: Jerry Higdon
Art Director: James Boone

American Country Christmas 1992

Editors: Patricia Dreame Wilson, Brenda Waldron Kolb
Assistant Editor: Lelia Gray Neil
Contributing Editor: Charlotte Hagood
Editorial Assistant: Patricia Weaver
Copy Chief: Mary Jean Haddin
Assistant Copy Editor: Susan Smith Cheatham
Designer: Melissa Jones Clark
Senior Photographer: John O'Hagan
Photostylist: Katie Stoddard
Production Manager: Rick Litton
Associate Production Manager: Theresa L. Beste
Production Assistant: Pam Beasley Bullock
Recipe Development: Elizabeth Taliaferro
Test Kitchen Home Economist: Angie Neskaug Sinclair
Artists: Barbara Ball, Connie Formby

Contents

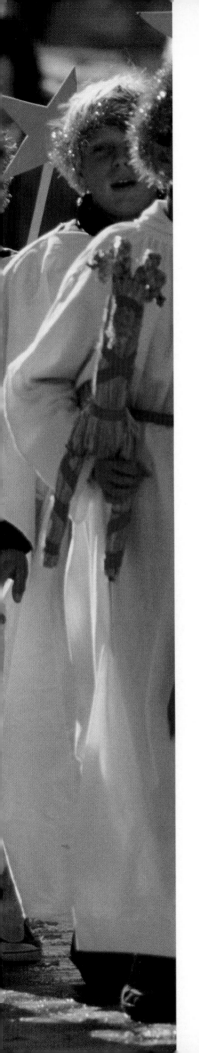

Wherever we may travel, our thoughts go home at Christmastime. ★ They may wander back to childhood and the sweet scent of Grandmother's gingerbread cookies fresh from the oven. ☆ Or to the sound of children, rustling their angel robes as they paraded down Main Street. ☆ Or our thoughts may drift to just last Christmas, when the children trimmed the tree with the family's special handmade ornaments. ☆ This new edition of *American Country Christmas* is full of such memories, waiting to be born. ★ Stir up a batch of silky, lavender-scented bath powder for a friend. Top the stacks of holiday packages with whimsical leaf fairies. Choose soft wool scraps to make old-fashioned ornaments. ☆ And travel from Alabama to New York, from Seattle to Houston, and back again to find new traditions to treasure. ☆ After you peruse these pages, you're sure to create a holiday season filled with heartfelt memories of home.

Patricia D. Wilson

Country Christmas at Home

Todd

Create a Woodland Tablescape

This Christmas season, carry your holiday guests away to a world set deep in the winter woods. Create an atmosphere that evokes the textures of majestic trees and the fresh scent of pine.

To pull together this rustic table setting, combine prized pieces from your own collection of country housewares and Christmas decorations with dried natural materials. By adding the woodland projects featured here, you'll be sure to give your guests a holiday fête they won't soon forget.

Holiday Leaf Tablecloth and Napkins

Materials (for 1 tablecloth and 4 napkins):
patterns and placement diagram on page 128
¼ yard (45"-wide) each of cotton prints: 2
    golds, 2 Christmas greens, and 1 dark red
1⅝ yards (45"-wide) Christmas red cotton
    print (for leaves and borders)
2⅛ yards (45"-wide) natural linen or linen-
    blend fabric
2 yards of paper-backed fusible web
7 yards (¹⁄₁₆") cotton cording
thread to match fabrics

Note: Finished size of tablecloth is 52" square. Finished size of napkin is 15" square. Wash and press all fabrics before using. All seam allowances are ½".

For tablecloth, trace 32 large leaves onto paper side of fusible web and cut out. Following manufacturer's instructions, fuse leaves to wrong side of each of 6 prints and cut out. Set aside.

From linen, cut 1 (45") square for tablecloth. From Christmas red print, cut 2 (9" x 45") strips and 2 (9" x 55") strips for borders.

To attach borders, with right sides facing and raw

edges aligned, machine-stitch a 9" x 45" strip to 1 side of tablecloth. Press seam toward border. Fold strip in half toward back of tablecloth, turn long raw edge under ½", and press. Slipstitch pressed edge of border along seam line. Repeat for opposite side.

For remaining borders, with right sides facing and raw edges aligned, center and machine-stitch a 9" x 55" strip to each remaining raw edge of tablecloth in same manner. Fold and press each strip in same manner, tucking excess inside ends of borders to square corners. Slipstitch folded edges closed.

Referring to photograph and placement diagram, position leaves on tablecloth, 1" inside borders. Peel paper backing from leaves. Beginning with corner arrangement and following manufacturer's instructions, fuse leaves to tablecloth.

For napkins, trace 4 small leaves onto fusible web and cut out. Following manufacturer's instructions, fuse 1 web leaf to each of 4 different prints and cut out. Set aside.

From remaining linen, cut 4 (15") squares. Lay cording just inside edges of napkin. Zigzag-stitch over cording, catching edges of napkin and pivoting at corners. Trim cording so that ends meet. Zigzag-stitch over raw ends. Repeat for remaining napkins.

In corner of 1 napkin, center 1 leaf 1" from edges. Peel paper backing from leaf. Following manufacturer's instructions, fuse leaf to napkin. Repeat for remaining napkins.

Left: Fashion a feast for the eyes with this holiday setting. The tablecloth and matching napkins are quickly made by fusing colorful fabric leaves to natural linen. The napkins are held by Nut Flower Napkin Rings, and the leaf motif is repeated on the spatter-painted place cards (see box at right). Winter Branch Candlesticks complete this inviting array.

Table Accents

Use pressed leaves and hickory-nut hulls to create two of the woodsy table accessories shown on the opposite page.

To make the place cards, press oak, maple, or other leaves to use as stencils. For each place card, lay a pressed leaf on heavyweight paper and anchor it with a small stone. Using an old toothbrush and red, yellow, and green acrylic paint, spatter-paint around the leaf onto the card.

To make each napkin ring, hot-glue six small segments from hickory-nut hulls to a purchased wooden napkin ring, arranging the segments to form a flower shape. Hot-glue the flat end of a hickory nut to the center of the flower. Lightly coat the napkin ring with a spray varnish.

Above: These spunky squirrels seem to be making a feast of our colorful acorn garland. Make the garland from purchased wooden acorns (available in craft stores) and four-inch strips of Christmas miniprint fabric. To "colorwash" the acorns, first add water to acrylic paints to thin them. Apply one coat of paint to the acorns and let them dry. Alternately tie the fabric strips and acorns to a length of jute string, securing the stem ends of the acorns with a drop of hot glue.

Fat 'n' Sassy Sideboard Squirrels

Materials for 1 squirrel:
patterns on page 129
carbon paper
1 (6") square of ¾"-thick pine shelving
band saw or jigsaw
sandpaper: 100 grit, 150 grit
nail
hammer
satin spray varnish

Using carbon paper, transfer desired pattern and markings to wood. Cut out, using band saw or jigsaw. Beginning with 100-grit sandpaper and finishing with 150 grit, sand all edges of wooden piece smooth.

For eyes, using hammer, tap nail through squirrel where indicated on pattern, tapping from both sides if needed for a uniform hole. Remove nail. Apply 1 coat of varnish to squirrel. Let dry.

Winter Branch Candlesticks

Materials for several candlesticks:
assorted tree branches, from 1"- to 4"-
    diameter
handsaw
electric drill with ⅜" bit
several ⅜"-diameter wooden dowels
wood glue
assorted twigs, about ¼" in diameter (for
    twig-covered candlestick)
purchased votive or taper candles
drill bit to match diameter of taper candles

For stacked branch candlestick, using handsaw, cut branches into slices varying in thickness from ⅜" to 2".

Using ⅜" bit and referring to diagrams, drill a hole through center of each branch slice. For variety, drill some as shown in Diagram 1 and others as shown in Diagram 2.

Determine height you want candlestick to be and cut a length of dowel this long. (Stacked branch candlesticks shown in photograph on page 4 are 9", 10", 12", and 14" tall.)

Select 1 of the thickest slices with hole drilled as shown in Diagram 1 to be base of candlestick. Put a few drops of wood glue in hole. Insert dowel and let dry. Stack branch slices of varying thicknesses onto dowel as desired, until candlestick is 1" less than desired height. For top slice, select slice measuring at least 1" thick, with hole drilled as shown in Diagram 1. Put a few drops of glue into hole of top slice and stack onto dowel. Let dry. (If top of dowel extends beyond top slice, use handsaw to trim dowel even with slice.)

For twig-covered candlestick, drill a hole through center of 2 (½"- to 1"-thick, at least 3"-diameter) branch slices as shown in Diagram 1. These will be top and base sections of candlestick.

For middle section, determine height you want candlestick to be and cut a 2"-diameter branch this long minus thickness of top and base sections. (Twig-covered candlesticks shown in photograph on page 4 are 5", 7", 9", and 11" tall.) Using ⅜" bit, drill a 1"-deep hole in center of each end of middle section. Cut 2 (2") lengths of dowel. Put a few drops of glue into each hole in middle section. Insert 1 dowel into each end. Put a few drops of glue into holes in top and base sections and insert dowels of middle section into holes. Let dry. (If dowel extends beyond top or base section, use handsaw to trim dowel even with section.)

To decorate middle section, cut small twigs into lengths that match height of middle section. Glue twigs, 1 at a time, around entire circumference of middle section.

Use either votive or taper candles with candlesticks. If using votive candles, melt a small amount of wax onto top slice of candlestick. Set votive firmly on top of melted wax. If using tapers, use bit that matches diameter of candle to drill a ½"-deep hole in top of candlestick, drilling through top of dowel if necessary.

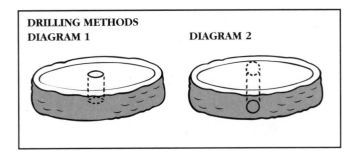

DRILLING METHODS
DIAGRAM 1   DIAGRAM 2

Below: This tablescape, arranged from a personal collection, offers a woodsy atmosphere in a twinkling. For this magical setting, Barbara Manning of Birmingham, Alabama, used soft green moss, twigs, bits of broken pottery, nuts, berries, and dried blossoms as a background for her hand-painted ceramic gnomes.

Above: With his staff and carved lantern, Father Frost seems to be setting out for an evening walk through the forest. His lantern is made from a poppy seedpod, but you could also use a small pinecone.

Father Frost

Dressed in a maple-leaf cloak and hat, Father Frost evokes images of wintry woods and snow-swept neighborhoods. This gentle figure will bring a sense of winter's wonders to an arrangement celebrating the elusive beauties of our coldest season.

Materials:
2 (2-ounce) packages of translucent Sculpey
 III modeling compound
emery board
acrylic paints: burnt sienna, cream, white,
 royal blue
small paintbrush
very fine artist's paintbrush
1 (16"-tall) green Styrofoam cone
sharp kitchen knife
florist's wire
hot-glue gun and glue sticks
glycerinated leaves: maple, oak, sweet gum,
 or beech (See "Preserving Foliage with
 Glycerin," on page 30)
white wool roving (see source listing on page
 154)
large poppy seedpod
craft knife
embroidery needle
rust embroidery floss
1 (14"-long) twig, about ⅛" in diameter

To make face from modeling compound, form a 2" x 2¼" oval that is about ½" thick at center and slightly thinner at edges. (See step-by-step photograph on opposite page.) Gently round front of face, making back of face slightly concave. With a toothpick, lightly mark a vertical line dividing face in half and 2 horizontal lines dividing face into thirds. Referring to step-by-step photograph, use modeling compound to form rolls for eyebrows and lips, ovals for cheeks and chin, and a wedge for nose. Place features on face, aligning nose with vertical mark and eyebrows and lips with horizontal marks. First use eraser end of pencil and then side of toothpick to smooth edges of features into face. Use point of toothpick to define lips.

To make right hand from modeling compound, see Diagram. Slightly curl finger section under, and leave a ¹⁄₁₆" space between thumb and finger section to hold handle of lamp. Repeat for left hand, except form thumb on right side of hand and leave a ⅛" space between thumb and finger section for staff.

Following manufacturer's instructions, bake face and hands in oven. Let cool. If desired, using emery board, lightly sand surfaces smooth.

To paint face and hands with acrylic paints, mix 1 or 2 drops of burnt sienna and 1 teaspoon of cream to make pale peach; paint face. Let dry. Paint cheeks with darker shade of peach and lips with burnt sienna. Paint "whites" of eyes with white. For pupils, paint a half moon in top center of each eye with blue; paint 2 tiny dots of white inside each pupil. Outline eyes with burnt sienna. Paint hands cream. Let dry. Set aside.

To make body, mark a horizontal line 2" from tip of Styrofoam cone and a second line 6" from tip of cone. Using kitchen knife, slice cone into 3 sections along these lines. Discard center section.

To attach top section (neck) to bottom section (body), insert 1 toothpick halfway into center of cut edge of neck. Centering neck on body, push exposed end of toothpick into center of cut edge (shoulders) of body.

To make arms, cut 2 (16") lengths of wire and twist them together to make 1 (16") length. Form a 1½"-diameter loop at center. Insert tip of neck through loop, settling loop around bottom of neck and molding wire over shoulders. Bend arms parallel to sides of body. Fold wire ends under ¼". Place a few drops of glue in each wrist socket; insert 1 wire end into each hand, making sure thumb is toward body.

To attach leaves, beginning at bottom of body section, glue leaves to body, applying glue first to leaves and then leaves to Styrofoam. Raising arms to shoulder height, arrange leaves in overlapping horizontal rows until body is covered from bottom to under arms. For 1 arm, apply glue to sides of 1 leaf; beginning at wrist, wrap leaf around arm wire, so that tip of leaf covers top of hand, and overlap glued edges of leaf to secure. Repeat, overlapping leaves, to cover remainder of arm and other arm. Glue large leaves around top of body and shoulders to cover tops of arms. Bend arms down from raised position.

Glue face to front of neck section, gently molding Styrofoam as needed for a good fit.

For eyebrows, roll a small amount of wool roving back and forth between hands to form a ⅛"-diameter roll. Cut 2 (½") lengths and glue 1 length to each eyebrow ridge on face.

For beard, referring to photograph, make about 5 long, beardlike tufts of roving. Glue ends of tufts close together along chin line.

For hair, make and glue additional tufts of roving to sides and back of neck and to hairline on front and sides of face.

To make hat, glue a leaf to back of head.

To make lantern, referring to photograph, use craft knife to cut vertical openings ½" apart in poppy seedpod. Remove seeds. Using tip of knife first and then embroidery needle, drill hole through stem of pod. Pass needle threaded with 6" of embroidery floss through hole, remove needle, and knot ends of floss to make a 1"-long handle for lantern. Slip handle over right hand, inserting handle between thumb and fingers. Insert twig between thumb and fingers of left hand for staff.

Above: By following this step-by-step photograph, you can easily model a realistic visage for Father Frost. Simply mark guidelines on an oval of modeling compound, apply small shapes of compound as shown, and then smooth and mold them until the kindly features of Father Frost emerge.

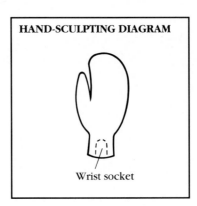

HAND-SCULPTING DIAGRAM

Wrist socket

One Woman's Treasure

A craft designer who transforms the ordinary into the exceptional, Charlotte Lyons incorporates her myriad creations into a family tradition for a spellbinding Christmas.

The spirit of giving and creating is a year-round presence in the Lyonses' Illinois home. In Charlotte's hands, bits of wool and ribbon, scraps of wood, and old buttons combine to make cherished gifts for every occasion. She confesses to a "nesting instinct that makes me save everything." Her decorating style shows this in groupings of turn-of-the-century prints, printer's type cases packed with odd pieces of family memorabilia, and shelves of brightly hand-painted china from the forties and fifties.

After years of painting folk-art pieces for her home and drawing pen-and-ink illustrations for greeting cards, Charlotte has begun focusing her design talents on a time-honored craft—rug hooking, using narrow strips of wool. (See page 36 for instructions for hooking one of Charlotte's designs.) Though the medium is quite a departure from her earlier artwork, she finds the craft of hooking perfectly suited to her simple, sensitive designs. (And she recycles old woolen fabrics in the process.)

Charlotte's search for rug-hooking fabrics led her

Left: At the Lyonses' home, family craft activities abound during the holidays. Charlotte passed her enthusiasm for sewing on to her daughters. Here, she shows Maury a few stitches, while Maggie chooses just the right trim. One Christmas, Charlotte painted the three cradles beside the tree—one to match each daughter's bedroom. She hooked the rug by the coffee table, showing all three daughters inside one house—safe and sound.

Inset above left: Charlotte's trademark—grouping family mementos and found treasures—creates a personal and welcoming atmosphere for the Lyonses' foyer. She hopes to collect and paint enough chairs (like this red one) for a whimsical dining room set. The Nativity scene beneath the tabletop feather tree was made by a Mexican artist. Maury's wool-appliqué jacket hangs on a flower hook by the door.

to several other interests. While rummaging through second-hand stores for used wool clothing, she came across other wonderful finds—such as antique feather trees, glass ornaments from the fifties, translucent blue plates, and an old battered bench that cried out for her fanciful style of painting. Bringing these things out of the dingy confines of a thrift store into her own artistic atmosphere became a challenge to her.

"Sometimes just rescuing it from the junk store is all it needs," Charlotte says. "It may look great just appearing in a different setting."

Charlotte's home-decorating style of arranging vignettes of mementos is evident in the scenes she creates in her recent wool designs. These use rug-hooking scraps for richly hued appliqué ornaments and clothing.

A notable example is her very first—a cozy wool-appliqué jacket for her youngest daughter, Maury. Lined with black-and-white gingham, the blanket-soft coat shows a white bunny hopping by a red-roofed cottage on one side and a little girl playing under an apple tree on the other.

Even when the designer was a little girl, she loved fabrics. Once her mother made decorative felt Christmas stockings with a matching tree skirt. The sequin accents and initials across the cuffs made the stockings glitter wonderfully. Later, Charlotte helped her mother in a small business, making decorated wicker purses.

"Mother was creative in a quiet way," says Charlotte. "And I was part of her admiring crowd."

And now Charlotte, too, has an admiring crowd, influenced by her style. After years of family decorating extravaganzas, during which everyone made ornaments for the tree, the family decided to turn this creative time into a gift-making tradition. Now each member of the family gives and receives handmade gifts.

Charlotte, her husband, Andy, and elder daughters Erin, 13, and Maggie, 10, make presents for the whole family. So, every December, there are conferences and secret discussions behind every door as the four-story Victorian house is transformed into a Santa's workshop. Even Maury, 4, who makes only a few presents, adds her continual encouragement from door to door. "I can keep a secret," she promises.

For Charlotte, making gifts is "a way to stay closer to what Christmas is all about. The dividend is that we spend more time with each other at home, where the meaning of Christmas rings true."

Above: Most of Charlotte's collectibles have a history. A friend once gave her five miniature sheep. The mixed flock of plastic, chalk, and rubber lambs has grown each year. The treasure-packed hutch itself is another of Charlotte's yard-sale finds. Good friend and fellow illustrator Mary Engelbreit painted the colorful reindeer in the foreground.

Left: Charlotte, the first girl born in her father's family in 50 years, was the recipient of her grandmother's crystal and silver. The Victorian heirlooms mix gracefully with her thrift-shop finds, such as the fine ivy-trimmed tablecloth. Erin and Maggie take turns practicing for an upcoming piano recital. Younger sister Maury, though eager, has a few years to wait.

Right: The intoxicating fragrance of paperwhite narcissus fills the Lyonses' home continually from Thanksgiving to Valentine's Day. Andy built the magazine holder that Charlotte painted green. She painted the tea-party bench to match. Years ago, she learned to work a jigsaw and made the bunny napkin holder.

Below: Andy did the renovation that transformed several rooms into one airy kitchen space. Another of Charlotte's house-motif hooked rugs rests in front of the oven. Charlotte says of the decorated refrigerator door, "My children's artwork is my favorite collectible. It's wonderful primitive folk art to me."

Memorable Mantels

For generations the hearth has been the center of holiday family gatherings. It is the place where people come together to share stories and laughter, and often, marshmallows and chestnuts. The mantel, therefore, becomes a natural focal point for holiday decorating.

This Christmas, unwrap your favorite holiday pieces, add a bit of creativity, and turn your mantel into a holiday showpiece. Whether it is decorated with an elaborate display of collectibles or simple sprigs of holly, your mantel is the place to capture the attention of all who enter your home.

Above: These lambs, lured by their lifelike cousins in the painting, have wandered far from their shepherd—and have come to grace this mantel for a gentle Christmas presentation. The impact of this display comes from its focus on one element.

Above: A neutral-colored mantel provides the perfect setting for this primitive Christmas scene. All of the pieces are antiques and are arranged to show Santa on his way to visit the inhabitants of the log cabin. A colorful garland of dried fruit complements the rusticity of the scene.

Above: Long after the Christmas season has passed, these birdhouses will remain on Dolly Walker's mantel in Birmingham, Alabama. The smaller two-story house was built by Dolly's youngest daughter, Katie, in Sunday school . Nestled among the fresh Southern magnolia leaves and juniper, these houses seem to have found their niche.

Above right: One Christmas, Dolly also showcased her collection of miniature rocking chairs and twig furniture by wiring them to greenery and pairing them with her antique dolls. Dolly passed down the sweet maiden in the purple dress to her eldest daughter, Kelly, who also enjoys collecting miniature furniture—the tea set on the tiny vanity is part of her collection.

Right: Dolly commissioned Roy Dollar, an interior designer, to bedeck her house in holiday finery. He combined various types of greenery, such as magnolia leaves, Douglas fir, and variegated holly, to decorate the mantel and adjacent bookcases. The combination of rich textures creates lush botanical appeal.

16

Left: In early America, homes were built with the hearth at the physical center; the family's activities took place around the fireplace. This log cabin mantel needs nothing more than a garland of holly and cedar sprigs, adorned with bright red bows, to provide a splash of color against the dark wood.

Below left: The owners of this Tennessee home did extensive research on Colonial American homes and followed the building specifications and designs from that era when constructing their house. The Williamsburg-red mantel comes alive at Christmas with the addition of whimsical antiques such as the hand-painted Santa and sailor dolls.

Above: Simplicity is often the best recipe for successful decorating. The delicate placement of these knitted baby stockings adds a nostalgic note to an otherwise stately setting.

Antiques Deck These Halls

Especially when the temperature dips low, a December-holiday visit to this Illinois farmhouse is a heartwarming event.

For 22 years, Darlene Lesicko, an antiques dealer, and her husband, Steve, an electrician, have worked on their 30-acre homeplace, built in 1863, to get the atmosphere they wanted. And their persistence has paid off in a comfortable late-1800s-style home.

Their passion for just the right period furnishings carries over into flawless antique Christmas decor. With a stocking from the 1890s, a rocking horse from the 1850s, and scores of hand-blown glass German ornaments, there is unquestionable authenticity. Darlene's eye for detail is the crowning jewel.

Darlene came from a big German family, and every year her home boasted a fresh tree overflowing with decorations. Now her own home has dozens of Christmas trees—each covered with a different style of antique ornaments. There is a small tree with only pressed-cotton figures and a rare, ceiling-high feather tree with all hand-blown ornaments. The Lesickos' daughter, Jennifer, decorates a tabletop tree with bouquets from her dried-flower business.

So that this enormous decorating task won't overwhelm her, Darlene has devised her own method. When she begins decorating, she unpacks the box labeled for the top of the first tree and proceeds with boxes labeled for that tree before continuing to the next one. After Christmas, she packs away each ornament in its proper box again.

Even when the holidays have ended, the Lesicko home glows with a year-round warmth that flames anew when Christmas returns.

Right: The Lesickos have skillfully created a comfortable country atmosphere in their Illinois farmhouse. Every ornament on the 1890s feather tree is an antique, like all the furnishings in the Lesicko home. The doll standing by the tree belonged to Darlene's mother. The red-and-white appliquéd quilt draped over the corner cabinet was made in the 1860s.

Above: The tabletop feather tree is decorated only with antique cotton figures, including Santas, a swan, and even a champagne bottle. The blue hutch is filled with a sample of Darlene's quilt collection. "My favorite quilts are definitely red, white, and green," Darlene says. Chalkware Santas accent the hutch.

Below: Darlene remembers her grandmother baking the distinctive anise-flavored springerle at Christmastime. Darlene's museum-quality cookie mold collection includes a very rare child's rolling pin. The larger molds, like the heart and the lamb, were used as cake boards.

A German Tradition

In southwest Germany in the medieval county of Swabia, *springerle* sprang forth. From the German tradition of sculpting bread into figures and symbols for festive occasions, the idea of a finely detailed, decorative cookie evolved. The evolution was natural enough, since the nearly unleavened cookies could be shaped and molded more intricately than the yeasty breads.

At first the carved wooden *springerle* molds had much more variety than the simply patterned rolling pins we see today. They included symbols from nature, such as acorns, a cluster of cherries, or a songbird. The artistic carvers also depicted gentlemen on horseback or crinolined ladies holding bouquets.

At the beginning of the 19th century, it was fashionable to embellish the cookies with many colors, though the pale straw color is more customary today.

An avid *springerle* mold collector, Darlene Lesicko also bakes the anise cookies for her holiday festivities. Here is her recipe.

Springerle Cookies

4 eggs
1 (16-ounce) package powdered sugar, sifted
3½ cups all-purpose flour, divided
½ teaspoon baking powder
¼ teaspoon anise extract

Beat eggs at medium speed of an electric mixer until thick and lemon-colored. Gradually add powdered sugar, beating until smooth. Gradually add 3 cups flour, baking powder, and extract; beat well. Turn dough out onto a floured surface; knead in remaining ½ cup flour to make a stiff dough.

Roll dough to ¼" thickness. Using a floured cookie mold or *springerle* rolling pin, press firmly to imprint dough. Cut cookie squares apart. Place on waxed paper and let stand uncovered in a cool, dry place at least 2 hours to set the design.

Place cookies on greased cookie sheets. Bake at 300° for 15 minutes. Yield: 6 dozen.

A Holiday Crescendo

For many people, Christmas preparations begin right after Thanksgiving.
Of course, not everyone can wait that long.

Raymond and Nancy Waites, designer and design consultant, respectively, begin decorating in early September. Following months of seasonal decorative layering, their home reaches a brilliant holiday crescendo in mid-December.

Raymond helped establish the country movement in decorating with his rustic home furnishings for Gear, a marketing and design firm he cofounded in 1978. His American Country style, which began with 18th-century pine cupboards, antique pottery, and the influence of simple Shaker style, has, over time, gradually shifted to a country baroque approach. Luxurious objects, such as silver and crystal, characterize baroque, while treasured collections,

such as antique quilts and hand-carved decoys, define the continued impact of American Country. Now Raymond's country designs contrast the elegant with the everyday, achieving an overall feeling of opulence, accented with dots of folk art whimsy.

For holiday decorating, Raymond blends his treasured country collections of quilts, primitive rocking horses, and dried florals with gold-leafed fruits and gold-lamé roses. Live Christmas trees don golds of every tone, from sparkling metallic to muted dried floral. Fruit and floral tones of red and gold combine with fresh-fir green to pick up all the colors of the Scottish shawl used as a tree skirt. Raymond also varnished and gold-leafed plain brown craft paper,

Below: The small tree at left is studded with sunflowers, hydrangea, and Alabama cotton bolls, creating zigzags of garlands. The other tree carries more color—dried pomegranates, paper butterflies, pepperberries, flowers, and gold silk leaves. Nancy Waites, a design consultant with a documentary textile gallery, collects fabrics of all types, including antique needlework and quilts, like the black-and-white baby's quilt at right.

giving it the sheen of antique leather, to use around the base of the trees.

To achieve this grand effect, Raymond and Nancy need a jump on the holidays. In September, they center their attention on the fall entertaining season in New York City. Raymond begins with autumnal vignettes in the living room wall cabinet and adds clusters of gold leaves to the six-foot weeping fig trees. For Halloween, he simply adds dried arrangements and decorations. Thanksgiving festivities bring out even more displays. Finally, the Christmas trees themselves are brought home and trimmed, ushering in the height of holiday decorating. "I'm one of the first to put up a Christmas tree and the last to take it down," Raymond says. "Once we left the trees up until April!"

On December 19, Raymond and Nancy celebrate their wedding anniversary with a black-tie potluck dinner. Since many of their friends leave the city for the holidays, the dinner is usually a small affair, but last year, to their surprise, a crowd of 125 packed their loft apartment.

Designed for entertaining, the loft is perfect at

these times. When the Waiteses moved to their home, they wanted to retain the vast scale and openness the large space offered. They gutted the structure and divided it into private and public space with the horizontal placement of the kitchen. Raymond recognized the kitchen as the center of entertaining and added sleek white deep-drawered cabinets to tuck away the clutter.

Creative vice president and designer for Gear, Raymond designs country-inspired wall coverings, fabrics, furniture, lamps, rugs—even books. The Alabama native works with select manufacturers, such as Robert Allen Fabrics, Old Stone Mill Wallcoverings, and Springmaid Sheets.

Still a firm believer in the classic country look, Raymond's spring line for Gear focused on neo-traditional design, using tartan plaids and paisleys. These also show up in his holiday decorating. Linen, faux finishes, stipples, and stripes, all in moss green and antique gold, lend an Old World air to country.

For 1993, Raymond plans a classic modern look— clean, but not cool or stark. The basic color palette will use tones borrowed from nature—the beach, seashells, shades of green, terra-cotta, and spice.

"I want the line to have a nurturing quality, to cling to friendly materials and colors, to use wood and earth tones," Raymond says.

Raymond shares his design techniques in a new how-to book called *Small Pleasures*, published by Little, Brown and Company.

Left: This Christmas tree commands center stage in the living room. To achieve the cornucopia effect, Raymond covered the live tree with decorative fruits. A mixture of antique sequined apples, spray-painted plastic pears, and dried pomegranates complements the floral combinations of sunflowers, red pepperberries, and dried hydrangea.

Below: A niche with paired pitchers illustrates Raymond's affinity for contrast. Here, in the living room wall cabinet, he groups heirloom silver with country terra-cotta and bright golden ceramic. Pinecone-and-berry clusters adorn the handles for a touch of Christmas.

Below: A Gear bear, complete with a special Christmas collar, rides one of Nancy's many stuffed animals. Raymond accented a twig wreath with gold and copper to double-frame an illustrated portrait of himself and Nancy.

Above: Raymond painted and gold-leafed these white plaster cupids to look like antique architectural finds.

Right: The view from the kitchen to the living room frames the center Christmas tree with heirloom silver in the foreground and dried roses, boxwood, and gypsophila above. The dried materials create a ceiling of potpourri, which gives the kitchen a heavenly scent.

Below: This hand-hooked rug is in dramatic textural contrast to the sleek faux-papered curved entrance. The garland of red Christmas balls adds a bit of sparkle, plus a faux-pinecone texture. The decor of the foyer changes weekly, to offer a special greeting.

Favorite Motifs Add Whimsy to Decorating

Fish and pheasant may not be customary yuletide symbols, but for the McGaritys of Birmingham, Alabama, one thing has led to another.

Free-lance interior designer Celia McGarity's theory of Christmas decorating dovetails with her theory of design: Use what you've got. "It turns out to be much more personal than when you always go out and buy everything," she says.

Celia has a unique collection that has found its way into her holiday decorating. When she and her husband, Marshall, first moved to their home several years ago, Celia chose a wallpaper with a pattern of lake trout for the kitchen. This simple choice led to an angling-oriented collection throughout the kitchen—fish plates, fish prints, even antique fishing creels. For Christmas, this grouping has migrated into the breakfast room, which includes a small corner tree decorated for the children, an evergreen arrangement in an antique creel basket, and a fish platter at each place setting.

The McGaritys' dining room decorating scheme began with a similar inspiration—the wallpaper. (Celia had chosen a tapestrylike Ralph Lauren wallpaper as the color foundation for the entire house.) This densely patterned floral paper set the tone for an impressive Christmas display. Celia established a pheasant motif—evident in the feathered centerpiece and dinner china. The luxuriance of the wall's rose pattern is repeated in the centerpiece's lush base of softly gilded fruits, vegetables, and foliage. She continued the gold touch with brass chargers under each plate and gold cording entwined around each napkin.

Celia skillfully mixes the old with the new. For country Christmas decorating, either fish or fowl sends a welcome message.

Above: Celia McGarity bought the pheasant-motif china on a department store sale table and soon afterward spotted the stuffed fowl. For this striking centerpiece, she elevated the pheasant, used a pheasant-print fringed scarf as a drape, and arranged hand-tinted gold fruit around the base.

Above: For the McGarity family—Marshall, Britt, 8, Celia, and Blakely, 5—Christmas is a time to add decoration to every room in the house.

Above: Celia always decorates a little tree in the breakfast room for the children. A string of outdoor patio lights forms the fish garland on the tree. The Indian blanket and buffalo plaid napkins add a western warmth.

Above right: A fine collection of antique fishing creels is brought to the fore (and aft) at Christmastime. The front door decoration (at top) incorporates raffia and fishing lures into the holly and pine. The back door (at bottom) welcomes neighbors with a fish wind chime to introduce the theme from afar.

Pick Poinsettias For a Fresh Look

Poinsettias—with their lush green leaves and star-shaped, traditionally red bracts—are exuberant emblems of Christmas. In America, potted poinsettias have become so standard a feature of the holiday landscape that they are almost as conventional as Christmas trees.

To give new flair to decorating with these old favorites, pick the individual "flowers," or bracts. Once you condition and insert their stems into florist's water picks (see "Prepping Poinsettia Bracts," at right), you can use the bracts as stunning accents in all kinds of holiday arrangements.

You might, for instance, take your cue from Lucy Wise of Springville, Alabama. One Christmas, as an early gift for her busy daughter and son-in-law, Debbie and Bryon Skellett, she decorated an extraordinary poinsettia-studded tree in their home.

First, Lucy festooned the 10-foot pine with white lights and garlands of twisting red ribbon. Then she added a collection of favorite ornaments. A great believer in taking advantage of the gifts found just outside one's door, Lucy also added pinecones sprayed with gold metallic paint and crepe-myrtle pods sprayed with burgundy paint.

Finally, for the finishing touch, Lucy tucked more than two dozen bracts of cherry-colored poinsettia among the tree's branches. The effect was sensational, and the tree looked cheerfully at home in Debbie and Bryon's living room, which sports the colors of claret red, bright white, and periwinkle blue.

For decorating other rooms in your home, you might follow the example of Pam and Paul Jones. Two Christmases ago, after 15 years of loving labor, they finally finished restoring their country farmhouse just outside Rutledge, Georgia. Naturally, they were in the mood to celebrate. With particular zest, Pam decorated every room, using variegated pink-and-ivory poinsettia bracts to give her arrangements a special spark.

In the dining room, Pam added greenery and several poinsettia bracts to a pinecone wreath and centerpiece, two favorites made for her by a good friend. Then Pam wired several more bracts to an elegant garland that she had fashioned from pine and fir boughs and accented with baby's breath,

Above: Lucy Wise of Springville, Alabama, has discovered the perfect plan for those tree trimmers whose expectations are greater than either their ornament collections or their budgets—creating ornaments from nature. Lucy used spray-painted pinecones and crepe-myrtle pods as well as fresh poinsettia bracts to decorate this showstopper tree.

pinecones, and graceful spirals of velvet ribbon. The Joneses' dining room is soft with blue-grays, deep pinks, and the golden tones of polished pine. Against this dusky backdrop, the ivory bracts glowed like stars.

As both Lucy and Pam will tell you, treating the poinsettias' stems and inserting them into filled water picks are simple steps indeed. And once they're nestled among tree boughs or tucked into greenery, the picks fade into the background, leaving, as the stars of the show, the stellar shapes of America's favorite Christmas flower.

Prepping Poinsettia Bracts

If you follow the simple steps described below, your poinsettia bracts will look fresh for weeks.

First, estimate the desired lengths of the stems you'll need for your arrangement; then, using a sharp knife and cutting at an angle, cut the stems accordingly. To seal off the milky sap, which can block the stems' intake of water, singe the stem ends with a candle flame for 15 seconds. Alternatively, wrap just the leaves and bracts in newspaper to protect them from the steam and heat; then immerse the stem ends in boiling water for one to three minutes. (Because the sap is a skin irritant and also poisonous, handle the stems carefully and wash your hands afterward.)

After treating the stems with heat, immediately plunge them, up to the bases of the bracts, in tepid water. Allow them to rest there for six to eight hours, or overnight.

Insert each stem into a filled florist's water-pick tube. (Also called water vials, water picks can be purchased at florist's shops and craft stores.) To decorate a wreath or centerpiece, simply bury the picks in the arrangement. To decorate a Christmas tree or garland, the easiest method is to rest the picks on broad boughs or tuck them into the foliage. For added stability, use short lengths of florist's wire to secure the picks to the branches.

Every two or three days, check to see if the picks need to be refilled. Misting the poinsettia bracts occasionally will also help to keep them vibrant throughout the holiday season.

Below: With poinsettias carefully placed from floor to ceiling, the dining room of Paul and Pam Jones is definitely dressed for Christmas. Paul, a craftsman of fine reproduction furniture, made the dining table, hutch, and huntboard. Pam, a quilt and craft designer, fashioned the fresh arrangements that decorate the room. The couple pair their talents professionally as well at The Barn Raising, their shop in Rutledge, Georgia.

Ideas

Decorating with Preserved Foliage

Among the trees and fallen leaves of the autumn woods, you can find materials for an array of Christmas decorating and craft ideas. Preserve what nature has to offer by glycerinating foliage, or use individual leaves as patterns for stenciling or stamping fabric or paper.

Above: To preserve a piece of Christmas past or present— perhaps a favorite Christmas card—showcase it in a simple frame enhanced with sparkling gold foliage. First, spray-paint a glycerinated leafy vine and single large leaf with gold metallic paint. Then hot-glue the vine around the sides and top of the purchased frame. To visually anchor the frame, glue the single leaf in a bottom corner.

Preserving Foliage with Glycerin

You can preserve the glorious hues of autumn for winter arrangements by soaking foliage in a solution of gylcerin and water. This will keep the foliage from becoming dry and brittle.

While the process is easy, timing is important. Plan to begin glycerinating in September, when leaves are green or just starting to change color. If September has already passed, you can still glycerinate; just look for leaves that are not yet dry.

Cut small branches from desired trees or shrubs. Oak, maple, beech, ginkgo, and elaeagnus work well, but you can use whatever grows in your area. Working with small quantities of foliage at a time, crush the ends of woody stems to help them absorb the mixture.

In a sturdy container large enough to hold the branches, prepare a solution of one part boiling water to one part glycerin (found in most drugstores). Stand the crushed stem ends in the solution and set them aside for 10 to 14 days.

Leaves will change color during this process. The type of leaf used, the previous summer's weather, and the time the branches were cut will affect how much the colors change. Golden hues, deep browns, or even silver or black

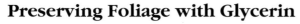

Right: Purchased wooden candle holders look their best when trimmed with other natural materials. Wrap a small flexible vine around each holder and hot-glue it in place. Seal it with a coat of spray varnish. Beeswax candles and a few glycerinated beech leaves complete this woodsy look.

may appear. Some leaves will retain their original color.

Remove the stems from the solution. (The solution can be strained and used again; if it has become too thick, add a bit of hot water.) Now soft and supple, the leaves will be ready to use in holiday floral arrangements or in the craft projects shown on these pages.

Left: Christmas fairies, lured in from the forest, are enchanting as package toppers or ornaments. Best of all, these airy nymphs are a breeze to make. To form the head and body, hot-glue the stem end of a large glycerinated leaf to the bottom of an acorn. Attach the wings by hot-gluing smaller leaves to the opposite side of the large leaf. Dress the fairy by layering the body and wings with small leaves of different colors.

To make a hanger, choose a color of pearl cotton floss that complements the leaves. Wrap the floss around a piece of nine-inch cardboard four times. Cut the last thread even with the cardboard. Slide the floss off the cardboard and hot-glue the end of the loops with the cut thread to the back of the fairy. Hot-glue a leaf over the glued thread to conceal it.

Right: Glossy green or white wrapping paper and brown craft paper can be easily transformed into holiday wrapping papers with the look of antique botanical prints. Take a walk through the woods or garden for instant inspiration, and then experiment with creative combinations of papers, paints, and leaves. Simply place pressed leaves on the paper and spray a light coat of paint over the entire surface, being careful not to move the paper or the leaves. Carefully remove the leaves and let the paint dry.

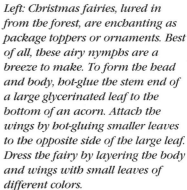

Left: Combine the reds and greens of outdoors with gold accents on these leaf-printed napkins for your holiday table. Sponge green acrylic fabric paint on the more textured side of a fern frond or a small stem with leaves. Place the frond, paint side down, on an all-cotton napkin. Cover the frond with a sheet of paper and firmly rub your hand over it. Remove the paper and frond. Accent the design with gold metallic fabric paint, or print berries with a pencil eraser dipped in red fabric paint. After the paints dry, follow the manufacturer's instructions to heat-set the colors.

Holiday Handiwork

Woolen Treasures

**Here is the opportunity that you and your wool scrap bag have been waiting for:
a cornucopia of Christmas crafts made with remnants of wool.**

Above: These folklike ornaments come by their old-fashioned charm naturally. Inspired by the penny rugs so popular in the 19th century, these variations are made of simple shapes from wool scraps and then secured, one atop the other, with blanket stitches. From left to right: Penny Square, Penny Diamond, Heart Sachet, Texas Star, Penny Flower.

A Quintet of Appliqué Ornaments

Materials for 1 ornament:
patterns on pages 138-39
1 (6") square of black, red, or turquoise wool
    or wool felt
pinking shears
scraps of wool or wool felt: black, red, green,
    yellow, lavender, turquoise, dark turquoise,
    tan
sewing scissors
embellishments: assorted sequins, green
    embroidery floss
sewing thread: yellow, red
small amount of Christmas potpourri (for
    Heart Sachet)
crewel needle
2 (6") lengths of ¼"-wide coordinating satin
    ribbon

Transfer pattern for ornament base to wool
square. Using pinking shears, cut out. Transfer appliqué patterns to wool scraps. Using sewing scissors, cut out.

Referring to patterns, sew on sequins. Using
feather stitch, lazy daisy stitch, and stemstitch, embroider appliqué pieces. (See Diagram.)

Referring to patterns for placement, position appliqué pieces on ornament base. For Heart Sachet,
tuck potpourri between ornament base and heart-
shaped appliqué piece before stitching. Using yellow thread for Heart Sachet and red thread for all
else, blanket-stitch edges of pieces to secure.

For hanger, fold 1 length of ribbon in half and
knot ends together. Tie remaining length into a
bow. Referring to photograph for placement, tack
loop and bow to top of ornament front.

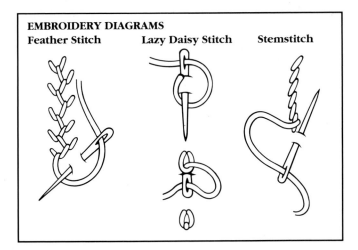

EMBROIDERY DIAGRAMS
Feather Stitch   Lazy Daisy Stitch   Stemstitch

Wool Gathering

Many crafters regard wool as the most beautiful of fabrics. And half the fun, they say, lies in building a collection of woolens that will one day be worked into gorgeous handmade objects. By recycling old wool gar-ments and blankets, and buying new wool for only select parts of a design, a crafter saves money and en-sures that her finished piece will have a rich variety of colors and textures.

If you are interested in creating your own cache of woolens, start by asking friends and family for their cast-off winter cloth-ing and wool blankets. Thrift shops, garage sales, and mail-order houses that carry new wool fabrics as well as remnants and "sec-onds" are all excellent sources for inexpen-sive wool. Avoid worsteds and wool blends, and look for tightly woven fabrics in a variety of colors and patterns.

Before storing your woolens, wash them with a harsh detergent in a hot-water wash cycle and a cold-water rinse; then tumble them dry. Known as "felting," this process tightens the weave to prevent raveling and therefore makes the fabric both easier to work with and more durable. (You may need to repeat the process once or twice until the fabric does not ravel.) Before washing the garments, remove the linings. After drying, cut off the waistbands, zip-pers, and pockets, and open all seams. Roll the pieces in bundles and store them in clear plastic bags.

Finally, don't be de-terred by fabrics with unappealing colors. One way to obtain just the right colors is to dye the woolens you already have on hand. To obtain the best re-sults, follow the in-structions of the dye manufacturer. Fabrics that are too bright or too dark to be dyed successfully can usual-ly be lightened, either by boiling in water mixed with several teaspoons of a laundry detergent that con-tains a bleaching agent or, if that doesn't work, by using a com-mercial color remover.

For the rug-hooking supplies and variety of new woolens that you may need to begin your next project, see the source listing on page 154.

The Art of Rug Hooking

The traditional art of rug hooking—the technique of hooking yarn or woolen strips into a burlap foundation—was especially popular in America during the mid-1800s. Thrifty women of this era cut their worn-out wool garments and blankets into strips and then hooked the strips into charming rugs that we prize today as true examples of American folk art.

You can learn this old American craft by hooking the Little House Ornament or its companion chair mat.

Before you begin, search your scrap bag for a variety of closely woven wools and flannels. The more colors and textures of wool strips you use, the greater the primitive effect of your final piece.

Little Hooked Houses

Materials for both hooked projects:
patterns on pages 140-42
burlap or monk's cloth: 12" square for ornament, 24" x 19" piece for chair mat
sharp shears, fabric strip cutter, or rotary cutter and mat
masking tape
tracing paper
black fine-tipped permanent marker
hoop or frame: 7" or 8" hoop for ornament; 14" hoop, or stretcher frame and thumbtacks, for chair mat
rug hook (or, for ornament only, crochet hook)

Wash and press all fabrics except burlap before cutting. Using shears, strip cutter, or rotary cutter and mat, cut strips in widths called for in instructions on page 38, cutting along the lengthwise (straight) grain.

To prevent raveling, bind edges of burlap with masking tape, or turn edges under ½" and machine-stitch. Using tracing paper and marker, center and transfer pattern to burlap, aligning straight lines of pattern as closely as possible with weave of burlap.

Stretch burlap taut and insert in hoop or tack to frame.

To hook either design, hook house first, beginning with door. Referring to pattern for color placement, select strip of required color. Referring to Diagram 1, use left hand (or right hand, if you are left-handed) to hold ½" or so of 1 end of strip against wrong side of burlap, next to outline of door. At same point on right side of burlap, use other hand to insert hook between burlap threads and pick up strip. Pull end of strip (tail) at least ½" up through hole to right side of burlap. Use left hand to keep remaining strip untwisted and flat against wrong side of burlap as you work.

Referring to Diagram 2, insert hook in next hole in burlap, catch strip, and pull up to form a loop that is at least as high as width of strip. (Determine desired loop height and keep as even as possible. To make taller loop, pull up on hook before removing it from loop; to make shorter loop, pull down on strip from wrong side of burlap.) Continue hooking loops, inserting hook in almost every hole of burlap for ⅛"- to ³⁄₁₆"-wide strips and in about every other hole for ¼"-wide strips. (Loops should be closer together on curves and at beginning and end of a strip.) Loops should touch one another slightly. If loops are too tightly packed together, burlap will be distorted and will not lie flat. Sections of strips that show on wrong side of burlap should be as smooth and flat as possible.

To finish a strip, bring at least ½" of end of strip to right side of burlap. Trim tails even with loops.

Loops can be hooked in vertical rows, horizontal rows, diagonally, or in curves—whatever suits design element best. For example, in each design shown here, door was hooked in vertical rows, grass or snow in horizontal rows, and roof in diagonal rows. Hook main elements of central design first and then outside border. Fill in background last, hooking from outside to inside.

Continued on page 38.

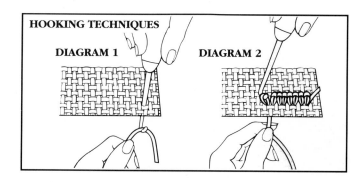

HOOKING TECHNIQUES

DIAGRAM 1   DIAGRAM 2

*At left and below: You can use even
your smallest scraps to make these
wonderfully woolly projects. The Little
House Ornament and Chair Mat are
booked with strips of wool fabric, and
the Spool-and-Wool Garland is strung
with circles of fabric that are less than
two inches in diameter.*

Little House Ornament

Materials:
4" x 6" pieces of wool flannel or felt: red, tan, green, brown, cream, light blue, medium blue
6" squares of wool flannel or felt: dark blue, black
hot-glue gun and glue sticks
12" (½"-wide) black satin ribbon
craft glue
pinking shears

From all fabrics except black, cut 6"-long, ⅛"- to ³⁄₁₆"-wide strips.

Referring to pattern for color placement, hook design as described on page 36.

For each snowflake, insert hook between background loops where indicated by dot on pattern. Each snowflake consists of 2 tails. Pull ½" of 1 end of 1 cream strip to right side. Insert hook in next hole and pull up rest of strip. Trim tails even with loops.

Remove completed piece from hoop. Machine-stitch ⅛" from outside edge of hooked design twice. Trim piece ½" outside machine stitching. Turn raw edges under and hot-glue to back of piece so that no burlap shows on front.

For hanger, cut ribbon in half. Fold 1 length in half to make a loop and hot-glue ends to top back of piece.

Using craft glue, center and glue house piece on square of black wool. Let dry. With pinking shears, trim wool ⅜" from hooked design. Tie remaining ribbon in a bow and hot-glue to base of hanger.

Little House Chair Mat

Materials:
12" squares of wool: purple, light brown, cream, dark green, light green
12" x 24" pieces of wool: red-and-black tweed or dark red, light gray, red, blue
72" (1¼"-wide) coordinating rug-binding twill tape
thread to match twill tape

From all fabrics, cut 12"-long, ¼"-wide strips.

Referring to pattern for color placement, hook design as described on page 36. Hook snowflakes as described in instructions for ornament, except make

each snowflake consist of 2 tails with 1 loop between them.

Remove completed piece from hoop or frame. Machine-stitch ⅛" from outside edge of hooked design twice. Trim piece 1" outside machine stitching.

To bind edges, with right sides up, place 1 edge of twill tape against edge of hooked design. Machine- or hand-stitch tape around all edges of piece. Fold tape to wrong side of piece and slip-stitch in place, mitering tape at corners.

Spool-and-Wool Garland

Materials for 2 (16") garlands or 1 (32") garland:
assorted scraps of wool fabric: red, gold, blue
pinking shears
8 (⅞" x 1⅛") wooden spools
DMC Medicis wool yarn: 1 (27-yard) skein each of red, green, gold, blue
craft glue
large-eyed needle
1½ yards of thin black cording
18-20 (4-mm) wooden beads

Using pinking shears, cut wool scraps into 90 (30 of each color) circles ranging in diameter from 1¼" to 1½". Arrange circles in stacks of 3, with each stack containing 1 circle of each color. Set aside.

Using a dab of glue to secure end of yarn to spool, wrap 1 color of yarn around 1 spool until spool is completely covered from lip to lip; cut yarn and use a dab of glue to secure end. Repeat with remaining yarn and spools to make 8 covered spools, 2 of each color. Let dry.

If making 2 garlands, cut cording in half. Thread needle with cording. Thread loose end of cording through and around 1 bead; knot to secure. Thread cording through 3 stacks of wool circles, a bead, a spool, and another bead. Referring to photograph, continue alternating stacks of circles, beads, and spools, as above, until all are used, ending garland(s) with a bead. Knot end of cord around bead to secure.

To make bear-and-heart or cat-and-mouse ornament: Using tracing paper, transfer patterns to fabrics and cut out. Using water-soluble marker, transfer all pattern markings to fabrics.

With raw edges aligned, pin bear or cat pieces together. Using 1 strand of thread, whipstitch pieces together, leaving open where indicated on pattern. Do not clip thread. Stuff through opening. Continue stitching to close opening.

Repeat for heart or mouse.

To attach ears to mouse, make small tuck at bottom of each ear and tack to secure; referring to photograph for placement, stitch ears to top of head.

Using 1 strand of thread and referring to pattern for placement, embroider eyes, noses, ears, and whiskers.

To finish bear or cat, wrap red ribbon around neck and tie a bow at front. For cat's tail, fold under ¼" on 1 end of black ribbon and tack to back of cat; knot other end of ribbon. For mouse's tail, repeat with white ribbon.

To make mittens ornament: Using tracing paper, transfer patterns to fabrics; do not cut out. Using water-soluble marker, transfer embroidery designs to yellow felt. Using 1 strand of pearl cotton, stem-stitch vines and embroider lazy daisy stitches for leaves onto yellow mitten pieces. (For stitch diagrams, see page 35.) Cut out, using pinking shears for green.

Center 1 heart piece on 1 yellow mitten piece; using 1 strand of thread, blanket-stitch to secure. Center yellow piece on 1 green piece; blanket-stitch to secure, leaving open where indicated on pattern. Do not clip thread. Stuff hand area. Using another needle threaded with 1 strand of thread, feather-stitch across wrist. (For feather-stitch diagram, see page 35.) Stuff lightly beyond feather stitching. Continue blanket-stitching to close opening.

Repeat for other mitten.

For hanger, fold under ¼" on 1 end of ribbon and tack to top of back of 1 stuffed figure. Repeat to attach other end of ribbon to back of other figure.

Playful Pairs

Materials for 1 ornament pair:
patterns on pages 142-43
tracing paper
scraps of wool or wool felt: 2 (6") squares of brown and 2 (3") squares of red for bear and heart; 2 (5") squares of black and 2 (3") squares of cream for cat and mouse; 2 (5") squares each of light yellow and green and 2 (1½") squares of red for mittens
water-soluble marker
sewing threads: pink, turquoise, and red for bear and heart; pink and turquoise for cat and mouse; red for mittens
size 5 lime green pearl cotton for mittens
polyester stuffing
¼"-wide satin ribbon for embellishments: 1 (12") length of red for bear and heart; 1 (12") length of red, 1 (6") length each of black and white for cat and mouse
crewel needle
1 extra crewel needle for mittens ornament
12" (¼"-wide) red satin ribbon for hanger

Above: Ned deftly shapes a vase on the potter's wheel in his studio. Two of the Foltzes' many cats investigate a vat of liquid clay. "The cats are part of the show," he explains.

Redware: A Foltz Art Tradition

During the first week of December, redware pottery collectors from around the country travel down the Pennsylvania Turnpike toward Reinholds, a Lancaster County farming community almost too small to have a name. Snowflakes may dot the windshields. Winter light washes the scene.

Once off the highway, the roads narrow and begin to wind. Still-green fields roll on, interrupted only occasionally by a large white clapboard farmhouse or a red barn.

Ned Foltz plies his trade among these rolling hills. He even shapes some of his wares from their true red earth.

Just to step inside Ned's shop and studio warms the soul. Dark burnished-red bowls, mugs, and plates shine with a rich glow, accented by swirls of mustard yellow and cobalt blue. Visitors are put at ease by the sweet scent of apple-studded fir garlands, the warmth of the old potbellied stove, the earthy smell of clay baking in the wood-fired kiln, and Ned's relaxed,

welcoming smile. At Christmastime, visitors are eager to step through the doors of this 150-year-old stone schoolhouse known as Foltz Pottery.

About a thousand redware collectors pass through the shop during this special Christmas show, to choose from an equal number of prized pieces of pottery. After months of preparation—sculpting fine stags, shaping covered jars, plates, and bowls on the potter's wheel, hand-decorating each Santa—Ned will have sold many of the best pieces by the end of the first day.

For thirty years, Ned has fine-tuned his skill of transforming red clay into impressive examples of redware pottery—pottery made in this county for more than 200 years. Traditionally, the folk potter's craft was primarily passed down through families, generation after generation. Occasionally, itinerant potters would travel from town to town supplying residents with their utilitarian earthenware. At that time all redware pottery was made from hand-dug clay and finished with a lead-based glaze.

Today at Foltz Pottery, only nontoxic glazes are used, and only select pieces are made from local red clay. The wood-fired kiln is supplemented by a gas and an electric kiln. These are Ned's few concessions to modern times in a shop that is steeped in another era.

Ned shapes his unique redware in three ways. Some pieces, such as the large Santas, are cast in old chocolate molds. The slab pieces are shaped by hand and molded over wooden forms into large oval platters. But the real collectors' items, such as the jars, bowls, and jugs, are wheel-turned and then hand-decorated.

Ned's personal interpretation of well-known Pennsylvania Dutch motifs creates the unique appearance of his redware pottery. He uses three different methods of decorating. Sponging a gold-colored clay on red or a white clay on blue, he makes a two-toned effect, also known as mottling. Using liquid clay, or slip, he draws floral, abstract, and animal designs on plates, platters, and pitchers. And he also decorates the redware by coating a piece with slip and then scratching a design into the surface to reveal the color underneath.

A collector himself—his grandmother gave him his first piece of redware when he was a teenager—Ned still travels to antique shows to buy an occasional example he covets. He must understand the feelings of the visitors who arrive so early on those December mornings. The back of the shop is open for them to enjoy coffee and doughnuts in the warm Christmas atmosphere created by his wife, Gwen. Once inside the shop, the difficult job of choosing just the right piece begins.

Above: According to Ned, Gwen is his best supporter. "She keeps me going," Ned says. When she's not working on accounts for Foltz Pottery, she creates her own beautifully hand-colored scherenschnitte *and wood carvings. (For our* scherenschnitte *projects, see page 71.) Baby, the big orange cat, and Lizzie, the gentle German shepherd, are always nearby in the shop.*

Right: Ned's wife, Gwen, works diligently on the business, but her creativity comes to the fore with lavish decorating for the Christmas show. Notice the garland of cookies cut with antique Pennsylvania cookie cutters.

Left: There is a great public demand for Santas and other holiday-themed redware. Father Christmas and the sheep were formed in antique chocolate molds. For more about Foltz Pottery, see the source listing on page 154.

Above: The furry finish on this brown bear was made by squeezing clay through fine screen. The technique is known as "coleslaw" because of its rough texture.

Below: Animals of all kinds can be seen in Ned's work, but cats are his favorite. Cat motifs were rare in old redware; the horse and bird were much more popular.

Above: Cross-stitched on royal blue Aida fabric, these ornaments are simply heavenly.

Celestial Cheer for All the Year

***In this double duet of cross-stitch ornaments and needlepoint pillows,
our friendly sun is the perfect partner for a sweet-faced moon.
Cross-stitch the two for ornaments you'll enjoy all year long.
Or, to create a stunning set of pillows, needlepoint
the designs with wool yarns in warm, wonderful colors.***

Sun and Moon Cross-Stitch Ornaments

Materials for 1 ornament:
chart and color key on pages 136-37
12" square of 16-count royal blue Aida cloth
size 24 embroidery needle
embroidery floss (see color key)
2 (6") squares of fusible interfacing
6" square of 16-count royal blue Aida cloth
6" square of ¾"-thick quilt batting
¾ yard (⅛") satin cording: topaz for sun,
   royal blue for moon
thread to match fabric
size 22 embroidery needle
embroidery floss for couching: DMC 796
   Royal Blue for sun, DMC 725 Light Topaz
   for moon

Note: Finished design sizes are 4½" x 4¾" for sun and 3¾" x 4" for moon. Unless otherwise indicated, all seam allowances are ¼".

Using size 24 needle with 3 strands of floss and stitching over 1 thread, center and work design on 12" square of Aida cloth according to chart.

Using mild soap, hand-wash completed piece carefully in cold water. Rinse thoroughly. Roll piece in a towel to remove excess water. Place stitched side down on a dry towel. Press with a warm iron until dry. (Do not use steam.)

With design centered, trim piece to a 6"-diameter circle (for sun) or a 5¼"-diameter circle (for moon) for ornament front. Using front as a pattern, cut 2 circles from interfacing, 1 from unstitched square of Aida cloth for ornament back, and 1 from batting.

Following the manufacturer's instructions, fuse 1

Continued on next page.

interfacing circle to wrong side of each fabric circle.

For hanger, cut 5" length from cording and fold in half to make a 2½" loop. With raw edges aligned and loop toward center, pin loop to top center of ornament front. Using a ⅛" seam, staystitch around circumference of front, catching ends of loop in seam.

With raw edges aligned, stack batting, front (right side up), and back (right side down), making sure grain lines on front and back are aligned. Stitch, leaving a 3" opening along top edge, with hanger loop in center of opening. Clip curves, trim batting from seam allowance, and turn. Slipstitch most of opening closed, leaving a ⅛"-wide opening on each side of hanger loop.

Insert 1 end of remaining length of cording ¼" inside opening to right of hanger loop; slipstitch this opening closed, catching end of cording in seam. Lay cording along seam line. Referring to Diagram and using size 22 needle with 6 strands of floss, couch cording, at ⅛" intervals, to cover seam line. At opening to left of hanger loop, trim cording to ¼" and insert end inside opening. Slipstitch opening closed, catching end of cording in seam.

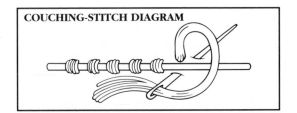

COUCHING-STITCH DIAGRAM

Sun and Moon Needlepoint Pillows

Materials for 1 pillow:
chart and color key on pages 136-37
18" square of 10-mesh needlepoint canvas
size 20 embroidery needle
wool yarn (see color key)
aluminum pushpins
blocking board
13" square of royal blue fabric for pillow back
thread to match fabric
14"-square pillow form
1½ yards (⅜") blue/gold twisted cording

Note: Finished design size is 12" x 12" for each. All seam allowances are ½".

Using 3 strands of wool and stitching over 1 thread, center and work design on needlepoint canvas according to chart.

Using pushpins and blocking board, block stitched piece.

With design centered, trim piece to measure 13" square. With right sides facing and raw edges aligned, stitch front to back, leaving 1 side open for turning. Trim corners; turn. Insert pillow form and slipstitch opening closed. Slipstitch twisted cording around all edges of pillow along seam.

Below: Needlepointed in warm wools and bordered with a luxurious trim, the sun and moon pillows add a vibrant note any time of year.

Stars, Stars, Stars

Age-old symbols of wishes made and promises fulfilled, stars are synonymous with Christmas. This holiday season, why not sprinkle these heavenly bodies all through the house? Arrange a constellation of Toothpick Stars on the tree. Scatter a few Wooden Stars alongside a centerpiece, or use them as bases for votive candles. Stitch up dozens of easy Perforated-Paper Stars and make them into ornaments, package toppers, earrings, and pins.

However you choose to use them, you'll find that you can make a whole galaxy in a twinkling.

Toothpick Stars

Materials for 1 star:
2 (1¼"-diameter) natural wooden cutouts:
  circles or ovals
wood glue
18 multicolored *or* natural wooden
  toothpicks
2 spring-type clothespins

To make guidelines for toothpick placement, use ruler and pencil to divide 1 cutout into twelfths. Cut 6 of the toothpicks in half and set aside.

Spread a thin layer of glue on marked side of cutout. Let glue dry until just tacky. Referring to photograph, place 1 end of 1 whole toothpick on each of the guidelines, with tips of toothpicks ½" inside edge of cutout. Place cut end of 1 half toothpick between each pair of whole toothpicks, with ends of toothpicks ½" inside edge of cutout. Apply a dime-sized dollop of glue to center of cutout.

Spread a thin layer of glue on 1 side of remaining cutout. Place second cutout, glue side down, on top of first cutout, sandwiching toothpick ends between. Clamp cutouts with clothespins and let dry.

Wooden Stars

Materials for 1 star:
pattern on page 128
4" square of ¼"-thick plywood
jigsaw
spray varnish

Transfer pattern to plywood. Using jigsaw, cut out star. Spray 1 side of star with varnish and let dry. Turn star over and spray other side.

Perforated-Paper Stars

Materials for 1 star:
charts and color key on page 135
1 (3") square of 14-count tan perforated paper
embroidery needle
embroidery floss and beads (see color key)
beading needle

Note: 1 (9" x 12") sheet of perforated paper will yield 12 (3") squares.

Using an embroidery needle threaded with 3 strands of floss and working over 1 mesh, center and work desired cross-stitch design on square of perforated paper according to chart. Using a beading needle threaded with 2 strands of same-color floss, attach beads according to chart.

Trim star 1 hole outside stitched design, being careful not to cut into any hole occupied by a stitch.

45

Holiday Crochet

Think of the tiny trinkets you could tuck into the crocheted treasure chests and the sweet surprises the cracker and drum could conceal. Gift boxes with real pizzazz, these crocheted containers also make eye-catching ornaments.

Crocheted Drum

Materials:
2 (218-yard) balls each of size 10 mercerized crochet cotton: red, royal blue
size 5 steel crochet hook
1 (1¾" x 6¾") strip of medium-weight cardboard
masking tape
1 (1¾" x 6¾") strip of plaid fabric or craft ribbon
glue
10 (¼"-diameter) gold jingle bells
large-eyed needle
½ yard (¹⁄₁₆") gold cording

Note: Crochet Abbreviations are on page 153. Use 2 strands of thread held together as 1.

DRUM BODY: *Rnd 1:* With red, ch 2, 8 sc in 2nd ch from hook, sl st in first sc. *Rnds 2 and 3:* Ch 1, 2 sc in each sc around, sl st in first sc. *Rnd 4:* Ch 1, (sc in next sc, 2 sc in next sc) around, sl st in first sc. *Rnds 5 and 6:* Ch 1, sc in each sc around, sl st in first sc. Fasten off after rnd 6. *Row 7:* (*Note:* Work back and forth in rows for rows 7-20.) With wrong side facing, join red around post of any st on rnd 6. Ch 1, sc around post of each st around, sl st lps in first sc, turn. *Row 8:* Ch 1, working through both lps of each st, sc in each st around, sl st in first sc, turn. Fasten off. *Row 9:* Join blue in last sl st, ch 1, sc in each st around, sl st in first sc, turn. *Rows 10-20:* Ch 1, sc in each st around, sl st in first sc, turn. Fasten off after row 20. *Row 21:* With wrong side facing, join blue around post of any st on row 20, rep row 7. Fasten off.

DRUM LID: With red, rep rnds 1-6 and rows 7 and 8 as for Drum Body. *Row 9:* With wrong side facing, join red around post of any st on row 8.

Ch 1, sc around post of each st around, sl st in first sc. Fasten off.

ASSEMBLY: Overlap ends of cardboard ¼" and secure with masking tape to form a drum. Glue plaid fabric or ribbon to inside of drum. Insert cardboard drum inside crocheted drum, positioning top row of sc so that it covers top edge of cardboard drum.

Referring to photograph and using blue crochet thread, sew 5 jingle bells along top edge of drum, spacing them 1½" apart. Repeat to sew 5 remaining bells along seam of drum base and body, horizontally positioning each bell midway between 2 bells above. Using large-eyed needle threaded with gold cording, pass needle just below 1 bell on top edge, above 1 bell on drum base, and so on, so that cording zigzags around side of drum.

To attach lid, using blue crochet thread, stitch a ¼" loop at center front edge of lid. Place lid on top of drum and slip loop around 1 jingle bell; stitch ½" of opposite side of lid (center back) to top edge of drum for hinge.

For hanger, thread needle with 1 (10") length of red crochet thread. Referring to photograph, pass needle up through 1 side of top edge of drum and corresponding side of lid and then down through opposite side of lid and top edge of drum; secure thread.

Crocheted Cracker

Materials for 1 cracker:
2 (218-yard) balls each of size 10 mercerized crochet cotton: red, green
size 5 steel crochet hook
1 cardboard toilet paper tube
red acrylic paint
paintbrush
2 (12") lengths of ⅜"-wide plaid ribbon
assorted trinkets and candies

Note: Crochet abbreviations are on page 153. The amount of thread listed above will make more than 1 cracker covering. Use 2 strands of thread held together as 1. Work back and forth in rows on base ring, except for rnds 12-14 and 20-22.

GAUGE: 5 dc and 2 rows = 1".

CRACKER COVERING: *Row 1:* With red, ch 28, join with a sl st in first ch to form a ring, ch 2, dc in

each ch across, sl st in top of beg ch-2, turn. *Rows 2-6:* Ch 2, dc in each st across = 28 sts (including beg ch-2), sl st in top of beg ch-2, turn. Fasten off after row 6. *Row 7:* With right side facing, join green with sl st in last st, sk 1 st, 5 dc in next st, sk 1 st, sl st in next st, (sk 1 st, 5 dc in next st, sk 1 st, sl st in next st) across, end with sk 1 st, sl st in first sl st. Fasten off. *Row 8:* With wrong side facing, join red with sl st in last sl st, ch 2, working in front lps only, 4 dc in same st, (sk 2 dc, sl st in next dc, sk 2 dc, 5

dc in next sl st) across, end with sl st in top of beg ch-2, turn. *Row 9:* Ch 2, dc in each dc and sl st across, turn. *Rows 10 and 11:* Ch 2, dc in each st across, turn. Fasten off after row 11. *Rnd 12:* With wrong side facing, join green with sl st in last st, (ch 3, sk 1 st, sl st next st) around, end with ch 3, sl st in first sl st. *Rnd 13:* Sl st into next lp, (ch 3, sl st in next ch-3 lp) around. *Rnd 14:* Sl st into next lp, (7 dc in next ch-3 lp, st st in next ch-3 lp) around end

Continued on next page.

with sl st in first sl st. Fasten off. *Row 15:* To complete opposite end of cracker: With right side facing, join green with sl st in any st on unworked side of foundation ch, rep row 7. *Rows 16-19:* Rep rows 8-11. *Rnds 20-22:* Rep rnds 12-14. Fasten off after rnd 22.

ASSEMBLY: Trim toilet paper tube to 3½". Paint outside of tube red. Let dry. Insert tube in crocheted cracker. With 1 length of ribbon, tie a bow around 1 end of cracker. Fill cracker with trinkets and candies. Tie remaining length of ribbon around open end of cracker.

Crocheted Treasure Chest

Materials for 1 treasure chest:
2 (218-yard) balls each of size 10 mercerized
    crochet cotton: red, green
size 5 steel crochet hook
scrap of lightweight cardboard
scrap of coordinating fabric
1" x ⅝" miniature lock or ½"-diameter button
tapestry needle

Note: Crochet abbreviations are on page 153. The amount of thread listed above will make more than 1 treasure chest. As a variation, gold thread may be substituted for green. Use 2 strands of thread held together as 1.

GAUGE: 5 sc and 6 rows = 1".

TREASURE CHEST BASE: *Row 1:* With red, ch 18, sc in 2nd ch from hook and each ch across, turn. *Rows 2-12:* Ch 1, sc in each sc across, turn. Fasten off after row 12. *Row 13:* With right side facing, join green with sl st in last sc, ch 1, sc in each st across to corner, ch 2, sc in each of 12 rows down side of rectangle to corner, ch 2, sc in each st across to next corner, ch 2, sc in each of 12 rows to beg corner, ch 2, sl st in first sc. Fasten off. *Row 14:* With wrong side facing, join green with sl st around post of last sc, ch 1, sc around post of each sc around, end with sl st in first sc. Fasten off. *Row 15:* With right side facing, join red with sl st in last sl st, ch 1, working through both lps of each st, sc in each sc around, sl st in first sc, turn. *Rows 16-24:* Rep row

15. Fasten off after row 24. *Row 25:* With right side facing, join green with sl st in any sc, ch 1, sc in each sc around, sl st in first sc. Fasten off. *Row 26:* Join green and rep row 14. Fasten off. *Handle* (make 2): On left side of chest base, join green with sl st in 4th sc from back edge on 4th red row from top edge, ch 6, sk 4 sts, sl st in next st, turn, 10 sc in ch-6 lp, sl st in first sl st. Fasten off. Rep to make handle on right side of chest base.

TREASURE CHEST LID: *Side Section* (make 2): *Row 1:* With red, ch 13, sc in 2nd ch from hook and each sc across = 13 sts. *Rows 2-4:* Ch 1, sc in each sc across to last st, sk last sc, turn. *Row 5:* Ch 1, sc in each sc across to corner, sc in each of 5 rows down side edge, turn. *Row 6:* Ch 1, sc in each of 15 sc across side and top, sc in each of 6 rows down side edge. Fasten off. Rep to make another side section. *Top Section: Row 1:* With red, ch 18, sc in 2nd ch from hook and each ch across, turn. *Rows 2-20:* Ch 1, sc in each sc across, turn. Do not turn after row 20. *Row 21:* Ch 1, sc in each of 20 rows down side of rectangle to corner, ch 1, sc in each st across to next corner, ch 1, sc in each of 20 rows across to next corner, ch 1, sl st in first sc of row 20. Fasten off. *Joining Sides to Top:* With curved edge of side section aligned with side edge of top section and wrong sides facing, join green with sl st in corner, sc through both pieces in each st to next corner. Fasten off. Rep to join remaining side section to other side edge of top. *Edging: Row 1:* With right side facing, join green with sl st in corner, sc in each st around. Fasten off. *Row 2:* Rep row 14 of Treasure Chest Base. Fasten off.

LINING: Cut a 1⅞" x 12" strip from cardboard and a strip of fabric ½" larger on all sides. Abut ends of cardboard and tape to secure. Glue fabric to cover the inside, overlapping edges and gluing excess fabric to back of cardboard. To support sides of chest, insert lining into base, creasing cardboard to fit corners. Cut a 4" x 4" piece of cardboard and a piece of fabric ½" larger on all sides. Glue fabric to 1 side of cardboard, gluing excess fabric to back of cardboard. Insert lining in lid, rounding it to fit.

ASSEMBLY: Thread tapestry needle with green and whipstitch top back edge of chest to back edge of lid. With red, stitch lock or button to center front edge of lid. Make a loop with 2 strands of red. Stitch loop to center front of chest opposite button on lid.

Left and above: Janice and Cary Bills had been married a year and a half before they realized how well their talents blended together. Janice has been a folk art designer since 1980; Cary was a home builder. Even now that their work sells around the world, Cary still says they are a "mom-and-pop" enterprise.

How a Single Birdhouse Paid The Bills

For some of us, sleepless nights come frequently with the onset of Christmas. So many last-minute details stare at us in the dark. But for Janice and Cary Bills, a sleepless night is just what they hope Santa will bring.

About two or three nights a year, Janice can't seem to get to sleep, but she doesn't spend much time tossing and turning. She gets right up. She knows just what to do.

"I get this stirring inside me," Janice explains. "I sit down to sketch and one sketch breeds another.

The next thing I know, I've finished 35 designs."

These midnight marathons are the design wellspring for CJ Bills, the company name for this husband-and-wife folk art team. Their home-based enterprise in Belfast, Tennessee, began with a single birdhouse design—a weathered-blue exterior fronted by a white picket fence. A simple sign that hangs above the entrance reads, "Welcome." A national magazine chose the birdhouse for its shopping page in 1985, and the orders for the Billses' work haven't slowed since.

"I bought a little old green birdhouse one day, and it just hit me that birdhouses were going to be big in the market," Janice remembers. "I still have that birdhouse. I'll keep that thing forever."

Janice and Cary's work has appeared in galleries and gift shops across the country and in catalogs such as Gardener's Eden and Horchow. They currently specialize in small whimsical furniture, including folk design shelves, benches, cupboards, and folk art paintings in Janice's own style.

"I always loved Christmas because there was a certain magic at that time," Janice says. "Now I can go to the easel to create that magical fantasy."

Right: CJ Bills has produced just about everything along the way, including this feather tree made by Janice and the barn-red fence made by Cary.

Left: "I always loved dolls when I was a child," Janice says. "Mother would make me rag dolls. One Christmas I got three dolls, and that was the most wonderful Christmas ever." Janice's granddaughter, BreAnne, calls this tableau "Grandmother's tea party." Cary shaped the tiny copper plates.

Below: The living room hutch holds a combination of personal work and Christmas collectibles. Janice painted the long-bearded Santa on a "scrap of wood I picked up in the barn." She also hand-lettered, painted, stained, and glazed the wooden Merry Christmas blocks.

Below: This free-form rose hip wreath holds three larger-than-life candy canes. The Billses no longer sell the crooked wooden canes, however, because, as Janice describes it: "You learn a lot as you go along with designing. Something can work great on paper, but it is much harder to produce."

"For every one fine artist who has gained recognition, there have been millions who in their own crude ways were artists," Janice says. "Fathers who found time to make primitive animals and pull toys for their children's Christmas; mothers (like mine) who, before plunging into their chores, found time to stitch a crude rag doll for a bright-eyed daughter who would not have been happier with a china doll."

Right: Cary made the blue-stained cabinet for this collection of antique shoes that he and Janice discovered at a nearby country store.

Bird Bowers

These whimsical birdhouses might be called bird bowers, or even chateaux des oiseaux. Anything but ordinary, they make charming decorative accents that are sure to attract attention. And creating these aviary masterpieces is easier than you might think.

These days, unfinished birdhouses come short or tall, straight- or slant-sided, with steep roofs or low, and they are carried by many craft stores, hardware stores, garden centers, and some mail-order companies. (See the source listing on page 154.) All you have to do is let your decorating talent soar and have fun transforming your plain birdhouse into a fanciful bird bower.

The Covey Condo, for instance, is gaily decorated with acrylic paints in three country colors. Gnarly, lichen-covered tree branches serve both as perches and landscaping. Finished with both acrylic paints and wood stain oils, the Copper-Roofed Cabin is topped with pieces of lightweight copper sheeting cut to fit with heavy-duty kitchen shears; copper tacks hold the roofing in place. The cabin's picket fence is made of strips of balsa wood that have been glued in place. The Bird Sanctuary is stained, painted, and decorated for the holidays with a darling dollhouse wreath.

You may find it hard to believe, but almost all of the materials used to decorate these fowlish houses were found in a single craft store and in the designer's own backyard. Even the wonderful Wren Cottage—with its moss-thatched roof, glycerinated-leaf siding, and charming acorn perch—had its humble beginnings as an unfinished, unornamented birdhouse.

So go ahead—plan to make several of these decorative *chateaux* for the birds. Besides making memorable gifts, the birdhouses can become intriguing focal points for mantel, doorway, or front-porch decorations. You might consider making a miniature version of your own home or a holiday bird hotel painted in your favorite Christmas colors.

However, if you want to hang your birdhouse outdoors in hopes of attracting a feathered family, you'll need to take a few precautions. Use rust-proof hardware and apply a protective finish to prevent the wood from warping. Make sure that the perch or perches are sturdy and will weather well. Also, drill a couple of quarter-inch holes in each side for ventilation, and a couple more in the bottom for drainage, to ensure that the baby birds' nursery will stay cozy and dry.

Painted Tin Angel

It's easy to paint the details that give this graceful angel her glow. Just follow the pattern, shading with darker colors as indicated. You might even consider matching paint colors to your holiday color scheme, or, if the littlest angel in your home is a blond or a redhead, surprise her with her own angelic likeness.

Materials:
pattern on page 143
tracing paper
awl
12" x 6" piece of 18-gauge or lightweight sheet
   metal, either tin or aluminum
metal snips
hammer
sponge brushes
metal sealer
acrylic paints: light blue, white, ivory, pale
   peach, gold, dark blue, red, brown, black
small and medium paintbrushes
metal varnish
12" (¼"-wide) blue satin ribbon

Note: If you plan to hang your angel outdoors, use oil-base varnish for final coat.

Using tracing paper and an awl, transfer pattern to metal. Using metal snips, cut out. With hammer and awl, punch a hole in top of angel for hanger. Wash angel in hot, sudsy water; rinse and let dry. When dry, sponge-brush metal sealer on both sides. Let dry for several hours.

When dry, apply 3 coats of light blue as base coat. Let dry for several hours.

Referring to pattern and photograph, transfer painting details to angel. Paint in colors indicated on pattern, using a slightly darker color and long, sweeping brushstrokes where indicated by small dots. Let dry several hours.

When paint is completely dry, sponge-brush metal varnish on both sides of angel. Let dry.

For hanger, thread ribbon through hole and knot ends to make a loop.

Right: A finished tin angel floats serenely in an ivy-trimmed wreath.

I love you,
Leigh Ann

THE GILBERTS

Sunbonnets in December

Sunbonnet Sue and Sam are decked in their finest Christmas calico and will delight fans for years to come. Whether machine-appliquéd onto a stocking or an ornament—or both, for a display that's twice as nice—this popular duo from the world of quilt designs will instantly add a country touch to your mantel or tree.

Sunbonnet Stockings

Materials for 1 stocking:
patterns on pages 130-32
tracing paper
water-soluble marker
⅓ yard (45"-wide) red pindot for stocking
⅓ yard (45"-wide) quilted fabric for lining
¼ yard (45"-wide) green checked fabric
scraps of solid green fabric
fusible interfacing
thread to match fabrics
6" (½"-wide) red double-fold bias tape

Note: Stocking pattern includes ¼" seam allowance. Appliqué pieces are full-size.

Using tracing paper, enlarge and transfer stocking pattern to red pindot and cut 1. Reverse and cut 1 more. Repeat for lining fabric.

From checked fabric, cut 2 (8½") squares for cuffs and 1 (11") square for body piece (and Sunbonnet Sue's arm). Following manufacturer's instructions, fuse interfacing to wrong side of 11" square and solid green scraps. Transfer appliqué patterns to fabrics as indicated on patterns and cut out.

With right sides facing and raw edges aligned, stitch 1 cuff piece to top edge of each stocking piece. With wrong sides facing and raw edges of bottom aligned, baste each stocking piece to matching lining piece. (Cuff piece will extend 3¾" beyond lining at top edge.)

Referring to photograph for placement, center appliqué body piece on stocking front and baste. Baste remainder of appliqué pieces to body.

Using narrow zigzag stitch, machine-appliqué basted pieces to stocking front through all layers.

For hanger, fold bias tape in half lengthwise and stitch along long edge. Fold in half to form a loop. On right side of stocking front, with raw edges

aligned, pin ends to left side of stocking cuff, 2½" from bottom edge of cuff.

With right sides facing and raw edges aligned, stitch stocking front to back, beginning at top edge of extended cuff piece, around sides and bottom, and ending at opposite top edge of extended cuff piece. Clip curves. Do not turn.

Fold cuff piece down to cover top edge of lining. Turn raw edge of cuff under and slipstitch to lining, 3½" from top edge of stocking. Clip curves and turn.

Sunbonnet Ornaments

Materials for 1 ornament:
patterns on pages 130-31
fusible interfacing
fabric scraps: solid and printed Christmas
**   fabrics, green felt**
thread to match fabrics
polyester stuffing
craft glue
3 (5-mm) red pom-poms
large-eyed needle
8" piece of monofilament

Note: Body patterns include ¼" seam allowances. Appliqué pieces are full-size.

Following manufacturer's instructions, fuse interfacing to wrong side of fabrics. Referring to photograph, transfer patterns to contrasting fabrics and cut out.

Referring to pattern for placement, baste appliqué pieces to body front. Using narrow zigzag stitch, machine-appliqué basted pieces to body front. Zigzag around body front just inside seam line, ⅜" from raw edge.

With right sides facing and raw edges aligned, stitch front to back, leaving an opening along 1 straight edge for turning. Clip curves and turn. Stuff body firmly. Slipstitch opening closed.

Cut 2 holly leaves from green felt and glue to hatband as indicated on pattern. Glue 3 pom-pom "berries" in a cluster at bottom of holly leaves.

For hanger, thread large-eyed needle with monofilament and stitch through top of ornament. Knot ends to make a loop.

From Paste To Pretty Presents

Using plain white paper and the simple paste-paint technique, you can create attractive hand-painted papers. Among the many craft projects you can make with your handmade paste papers are these one-of-a-kind gift boxes.

Above: The hand-decorated papers used to fashion these gift boxes—the Fold-Top Box, at left, and the Flower-Top Box, at right—were made with cornstarch paste, a bit of paint, a couple of household tools, and a dash of imagination.

Paste Paper and How to Make It

The paste-paint technique allows you to impart both color and pattern to plain white paper—all in one easy process.

To ensure your success, work with paper that is not too absorbent, such as bond paper, drawing or charcoal paper, art craft paper, gift-wrapping paper, postcard-weight paper, or posterboard.

First, make the paste: In a saucepan, mix two tablespoons of cornstarch with two tablespoons of cold water to form a paste. Add one cup of boiling water. Bring the mixture to a boil, stirring constantly, and boil until the mixture is the consistency of cooked pudding (before pudding is chilled). Cool. If lumps form, strain the paste through a fine sieve or an old nylon stocking.

To color the paste, add a small amount of acrylic paint and stir well.

Using a damp sponge, lightly moisten the surface of the paper. Using a wide paintbrush or sponge brush, evenly apply the paste paint, working the paint in one direction.

While the paint is still wet, stamp, scrape, or comb the surface to create a pleasing pattern. To stamp a pattern onto the paper, press the desired stamping object into the paint and lift off. Be creative in your choice of stamping object—carved potatoes, string, corks, buttons, wood or linoleum printing blocks, plastic cookie cutters, and natural objects such as feathers, shells, and leaves are just a few of the possibilities. To make continuous, flowing designs, drag a comb in wavelike patterns across the paint at even intervals, as shown in the photograph at left. You can easily make a homemade cardboard comb, with the teeth spaced to give the desired effect, or try the same technique with a plastic fork.

Allow your papers to dry overnight and then spray them with an acrylic paper fixative or spray varnish.

Fold-Top Box

Materials:
1 (3½" x 9½") piece of chipboard or medium-weight cardboard
craft knife
1 (4½" x 10¾") piece of heavyweight paper in color that complements paste paper
craft glue
1 (3½" x 9¾") piece of paste paper (see "Paste Paper and How to Make It," on opposite page)
bottom of 3½" x 3½" x 1" cardboard jewelry box
⅝ yard of heavy gold string

Note: The jewelry box used here is a standard size found in most department stores. If you use a larger or smaller box, adjust chipboard and paste-paper dimensions accordingly.

Referring to Diagram, use a craft knife to cut 5 chipboard pieces in dimensions indicated.

For cover, referring to Diagram for placement, glue chipboard pieces to colored paper, leaving 1/16" space between chipboard pieces and a ½" margin around all outside edges of chipboard pieces. Fold 4 corners of colored paper over chipboard corners as indicated by dotted lines and glue in place. Fold long edges of colored paper over chipboard and glue in place. Repeat with ends of colored paper.

Center and glue paste paper on uncovered side of chipboard pieces. Weight with a heavy object and let dry. With paste-paper side down, lay cover on a flat surface. On colored-paper side, center and glue bottom of jewelry box on center chipboard panel. Glue adjacent narrow chipboard panels to sides of box. Let dry. Fold and overlap panels over top of box to form lid and tie with gold string.

Flower-Top Box

Materials:
pattern and placement diagram on page 144
tracing paper
1 (11" x 17") piece of paste paper made with lightweight cardboard (see "Paste Paper and How to Make It," on opposite page)
craft glue

Using tracing paper and referring to placement diagram, transfer pattern to unpainted side of cardboard and cut out box.

Referring to placement diagram and using a dull, pointed object, crease box along dotted lines. Fold box on crease lines and glue tab to inside of panel 4.

To make bottom, fold panels B and D toward inside of box. Apply glue to inside of panels A and C, and interlock panels as indicated in Diagram 1. Hold in place until glue is dry.

To close top of box, fold numbered petals as follows: Fold petal 1 down slightly; petal 2 under 1 (see Diagram 2); petal 3 under 2; and petal 4 under 3 (see Diagram 3).

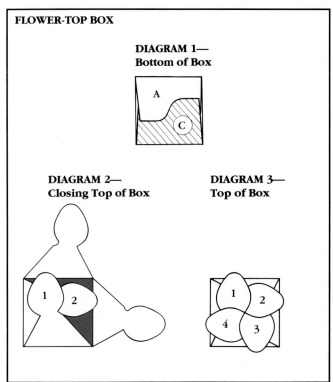

FLOWER-TOP BOX

DIAGRAM 1—
Bottom of Box

DIAGRAM 2—
Closing Top of Box

DIAGRAM 3—
Top of Box

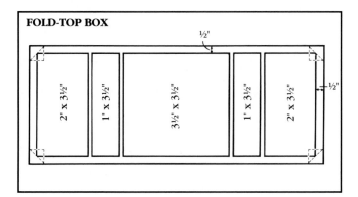

FOLD-TOP BOX

½"

2" x 3½" 1" x 3½" 3½" x 3½" 1" x 3½" 2" x 3½" ½"

Stately Snow Goose

Elegant curves, bright button eyes, and the softness of wool flannel make this graceful goose both regal and huggable. Once you discover how cozy this snow goose can make a favorite fireside chair, you'll want to stitch a pair—a goose to give away and a gander to keep for your very own.

Materials:
patterns on pages 134-35
tracing paper
⅔ yard (54"-wide) white wool flannel
scrap of rust wool felt
thread to match fabrics
polyester stuffing
wooden dowel (for stuffing tool)
long needle
black quilting thread
2 (⁵⁄₁₆") black buttons
1 yard (1½"-wide) red plaid ribbon
sprig of artificial holly (optional)

Note: Patterns include ¼" seam allowances.

Using tracing paper, enlarge and transfer patterns to fabrics and cut out.

For 1 side of goose, referring to pattern, staystitch where indicated on lower body, ¼" from bottom edge. In same manner, staystitch along bottom edge of upper body where indicated. Clip curves and press under seam allowance along this edge.

Aligning raw edges, lay 1 beak piece on right side of upper body piece where indicated on pattern; edgestitch beak in place just inside placement line. Trim away excess flannel under beak, leaving seam allowance.

With right sides up and side edges aligned, overlap pressed edge of upper body ¼" on lower body and pin. Position upper body piece as needed so that neck is vertical (see photograph). Edgestitch through both layers.

Repeat all steps for other side of goose.

With right sides facing and raw edges aligned, stitch goose pieces together, leaving open where indicated on pattern. Clip curves, trim seam allowances even, and turn.

Stuff firmly, using dowel to stuff hard-to-reach places. Slipstitch opening closed.

To attach buttons for eyes, thread long needle with quilting thread, pulling ends even. Referring to pattern for placement, attach buttons, pulling thread taut. Knot ends to secure thread. Tie ribbon in bow around neck. If desired, tuck holly inside bow knot.

Apple Tree Skirt

Wonderfully rustic shades of red and green give this ruffled tree skirt its Christmas tone, while the appliquéd apples with yarn-tied stems give it country charm.

Materials:
patterns on page 133
tissue paper
pushpin
1 yard of string
1¼ yards (45"-wide) Williamsburg green cotton print for skirt top
2½ yards (45"-wide) matching fabric for backing and binding
45" square of quilt batting
1½ yards of fusible interfacing
tracing paper
½ yard (45"-wide) brick red cotton for apples
⅛ yard (45"-wide) dark green cotton for leaves
scraps of light brown cotton for stems
thread to match fabrics
7 (14") lengths of light brown yarn for bows
4 yards (¼"-wide) brick red corded piping
2¼ yards (45"-wide) coordinating Williamsburg green cotton print for ruffle
⅔ yard (⅜"-wide) light brown ribbon

Note: Unless otherwise indicated, all seam allowances are ½". Instructions are given for machine appliqué. If you wish to appliqué by hand, add ¼" seam allowance to pattern pieces and turn under seam allowance before appliquéing.

For skirt pattern, tape sheets of tissue paper together to make a 60" square. Referring to Diagram 1 on page 60, fold square in half and then into fourths.

To mark circle, secure pushpin to 1 end of string. Secure pushpin at folded corner of tissue. Measure 22" of string and tie loose end of string to pencil to make a compass. Holding string taut, draw an arc with a 22" radius on folded tissue. Cut out through *all* layers of tissue. To mark inner circle, draw an arc with a 3" radius in same manner but do *not* cut out yet. Unfold pattern.

Using pattern, cut out skirt, backing, and batting.

Lay skirt flat. Using water-soluble marker, draw a straight line from outer edge to inner circle for opening but do not cut.

Following manufacturer's instructions, fuse interfacing to wrong side of appliqué fabrics. Using tracing paper, transfer appliqué patterns to fabrics and cut out. Referring to photograph, position appliqué pieces evenly around skirt.

Referring to Diagram 2 on page 60 and using *Continued on next page.*

matching thread, machine-appliqué pieces in the following order: apple, lower apple detail, bottom leaf, top leaf (closest to apple), stem, and stem detail. Stitch across stem as indicated on pattern. For each apple, tie a length of yarn into a bow and tack to bottom of stem.

Stack backing, right side down; batting; and skirt, right side up. Baste. Referring to Diagram 3, topstitch through all layers ¼" from outside of inner circle and along both sides of opening. Cut along marked line for opening only, stopping at edge of inner circle.

Around outside edge of each apple, topstitch through all layers, stitching as close as possible to machine appliqué.

With right sides facing and raw edges aligned, baste piping to outer edge of skirt top, beginning and ending at opening.

To make ruffle, cut 13"-wide strips across width of fabric, piecing as needed to equal 7½ yards. With wrong sides facing and raw edges aligned, fold strip in half lengthwise; press. Run a gathering stitch along long raw edge; gather to fit outer edge of skirt. With right sides facing and raw edges aligned, baste ruffle to skirt, sewing along stitching line of piping.

To bind raw edges of ruffle on inside of skirt, cut 2½"-wide bias strips from remaining binding fabric, piecing as needed to equal 4 yards. With right sides facing and raw edges aligned, stitch 1 long edge of bias strip to seam allowance of ruffle along seam line. Fold under ½" along remaining long raw edge of binding. Fold binding over raw edge of ruffle and blindstitch to backing.

Cut out inner circle along marked line. To bind raw edges of skirt opening and ruffle, cut 2 (1½" x 25") bias strips from binding fabric. With right sides facing and raw edges aligned, center and stitch 1 strip to 1 side of opening and ruffle, using ¼" seam. Turn under ends of strip. Turn under ½" along remaining long raw edge of binding. Fold binding over raw edge of opening and ruffle and blindstitch binding to backing and ruffle. Repeat for other side of opening.

To bind edges of inner circle, cut 1½"-wide bias strips, piecing as needed to equal 26". Using ¼" seam, bind raw edges in manner above.

To make ribbon ties, cut ribbon in half. Turn under ½" on 1 end of 1 length of ribbon and stitch to corner of inner circle on skirt top. Repeat for other side.

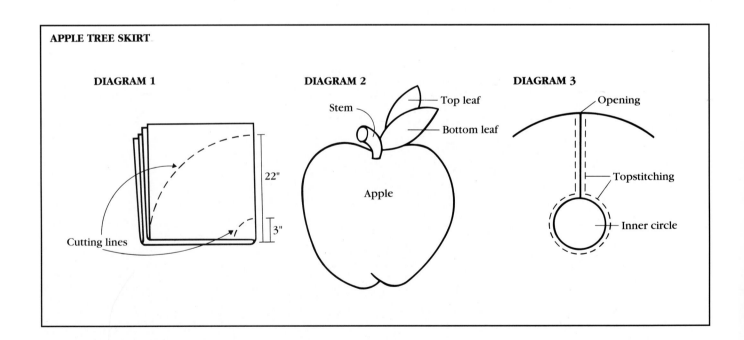

APPLE TREE SKIRT

DIAGRAM 1

22"

3"

Cutting lines

DIAGRAM 2

Stem

Top leaf

Bottom leaf

Apple

DIAGRAM 3

Opening

Topstitching

Inner circle

Christmas Booties

Made with a few scraps of calico and lots of tender loving care, these holiday booties will keep your little one's toes warm this year. Next year, attach matching ribbons and hang the booties from your tree, or place them on a table or mantle as a loving reminder of baby's first Christmas.

Materials for 1 pair of booties:
patterns on page 129
tracing paper
⅛ yard (45"-wide) green Christmas print
⅛ yard (45"-wide) red Christmas print for lining
scraps of red cotton fabric
scraps of thin batting
thread to match fabrics
large-eyed embroidery needle
green embroidery floss

Note: Except where noted, patterns include ¼" seam allowances.

Using tracing paper, transfer patterns and markings to fabrics and cut out. Clip ⅛" into seam allowance at B on fabric and batting uppers.

For 1 bootie: To make upper, with right sides facing and raw edges aligned, stitch green print upper pieces together from A to B and then from C to D. Turn. Repeat with red print lining and batting upper pieces, but do not turn. Trim seam allowance on batting upper to ⅛". With right sides facing and raw edges aligned, slip 1 green print upper inside red print upper. With wrong sides facing, slip batting upper inside green print upper. To join layers, stitch around top edge of upper, beginning at D, reinforcing seam with several backstitches at B, and ending at D. Trim batting from seam allowance and clip curves. Turn so that wrong sides of green fabric and batting are facing, with batting on outside. Pull lining out of the way through top edge of upper, wrong side out.

To join sole to upper: With raw edges aligned, pin 1 batting sole piece to wrong side of 1 green

print sole. With right sides facing and raw edges aligned, pin green print/batting sole to green print/batting layers of 1 upper. Stitch all around sole. Trim batting from seam allowance and clip curves. With right sides facing, pin 1 lining sole piece to lining upper. Stitch all around sole, leaving a 1¾" opening on side of sole. Clip curves and turn lining and bootie right side out, through opening in lining. Slipstitch opening closed. Tuck lining inside bootie. Roll top edge down to form cuff.

Repeat to make second bootie.

To make heart appliqué shapes, trace large heart pattern on wrong side of scrap of red fabric. With right sides facing, place on top of a second scrap of red fabric and machine-stitch along traced line. Adding ⅛" seam allowance, cut out heart shape. Clip curves. Make a slash in back layer of heart only and turn right side out. Press heart and slipstitch opening closed. Repeat to make another large heart. In same manner, make 2 small hearts from red print lining fabric.

To appliqué heart shapes to booties, referring to photograph for placement, appliqué 1 large heart shape to front of 1 bootie. Center and appliqué 1 small heart shape to large heart. Using 2 strands of floss, stemstitch around edge of each heart shape. (See page 35 for stemstitch diagram.) Repeat for remaining bootie.

Ideas

Candlelight Creations

Warm your heart and home with the soft glow of candles. Make your own candles to illuminate your holiday table with an old-fashioned spirit.

Above: Make the beribboned gift box candle in a tried-and-true way. Tie a length of wick around a pencil and hang it over the center of an empty pint-sized milk carton. Pour melted wax into the carton and let it harden to form a cube. Add strips of decorating wax to the block to create the effect of ribbons. To make the star candles, join two molded stars with a coating of melted wax, sandwiching a length of wick in between. Then apply strips of decorating wax around the seams. For information on ordering candle-decorating wax, see the source listing on page 154.

The use of candles during Christmas celebrations has a rich history. Thousands of years ago the Romans exchanged candles at Saturnalia, their winter celebration, as an expression of good will. Christians adopted the Jewish tradition of the Feast of Lights to celebrate the birth of Christ.

This Christmas, continue the tradition by creating candles of your own. Some of the candles shown here begin as purchased candles which are then decorated; others are made at home, using melted wax.

Depending on which type of candles you are making, you will need to gather some or all of the following materials for your candle-making session: several old skillets, pots, and pans of assorted weights, beeswax, candle-making thermometer, coloring chips, old nylon knee-high stockings, assorted metal pastry molds, large plastic candy/candle molds, ice pick or wicking needle, and braided wick. (For information on ordering some of these supplies, see the source listing on page 154.)

★ To melt the wax, use cookware that you will not be using again for food (search garage sales and flea markets). Make sure cookware is clean and thoroughly dry before melting wax in it.

★ For a wax that retains dye, burns well, and produces little smoke, use a 50-50 ratio of paraffin to beeswax.

★ The bottom of a beeswax block often has a layer of dirt on it. Scrape off as much dirt as possible before melting it. If you find dirt sediment after melting the wax, strain the wax by stretching the top band of a nylon stocking over the pot and pouring the wax through the stocking.

★ To melt the wax, break the wax into large chunks and place it in the top of a double boiler. (You can make your own double boiler by placing a small pot in a large one.) Make sure there is always water in the bottom pan. If too much water evaporates, add more boiling water to the pan, being very careful not to splash any water in the wax. Melt the wax on medium heat, stirring occasionally.

★ Use a candle thermometer to check the temperature of the wax until it reaches 160°. If the wax becomes too hot, remove it from the heat and let it cool to 160°.

★ To color the wax, follow the manufacturer's directions to dissolve color chips in the melted wax (one chip will color one pound of wax).

★ Candle-decorating wax, used to trim the purple candle and star candles on the opposite page, is sold in very thin, brightly colored sheets. The wax is pliable enough to cut and bend into shapes. To make the wax adhere to a candle, simply press the desired wax shapes against the surface of the candle.

Candles in Molds

To make molded candles, choose a candy or pastry mold that is wider at the mouth than at the base so that the candle can easily pop out of the mold. (Search garage sales for interesting molds or see the source listing on page 154 for information on ordering candle molds.)

For each candle, pour the strained wax into a clean, dry mold. Gently shake or tap the mold to release any air bubbles and let the wax set at room temperature until hardened. Gently tap the base and sides of the mold with a wooden spoon or against the countertop to release the candle from the mold.

To insert a wick into the molded candles, cut a length of wick long enough to extend ½ inch beyond the top and bottom of the finished candle. "Cure" the wick by dipping it once in melted wax. Heat the end of an ice pick or wicking needle by immersing it in boiling water or by holding it directly over the flame of a gas stovetop. Pierce the center of the candle from top to bottom. Thread the wick through the hole. Fold the end of the wick against the underside of the candle and secure with a drop of melted wax.

Above: The simple elegance of pressed viola, rose petals, and miniature ivy turns these purchased candles into Victorian treasures. Carefully place a flower on one side of the candle surface. To attach the flower, heat the back of a spoon and rub it across the flower. Continue attaching flowers around all sides of the candle.

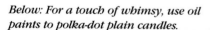

Below: For a touch of whimsy, use oil paints to polka-dot plain candles.

Safety Precautions

Never leave wax over heat unattended. If wax begins to smoke, remove from heat immediately. Let cool slightly; then slowly heat again.

If wax begins to flame, cover pot with a metal lid to suffocate the flame. DO NOT pour water over flame.

Do not pour melted wax down the sink. Add water to the unused portion of the melted wax. The wax will float to the top of the water. After the wax hardens, it can then be lifted easily from the pot.

Treasured Traditions

Left: Nothing could be sweeter for a new baby girl than these hand-knitted mittens and stockings, embellished with duplicate-stitched flowers of the prettiest pink. After she has outgrown them, hang the set on the Christmas tree as a sentimental keepsake.

Below: This Christmas, delight the mother of a new baby boy with these creamy-soft mittens and stockings that you have crocheted with love.

Baby's First Christmas

Christmas is always a time when lasting memories are made. For the family blessed with a new baby, this holds especially true, and the projects featured here are perfect for marking the occasion. Penelope Bear will charm the hearts of all who hold her. The adorable crocheted and knitted stockings and matching mittens will keep the little one warm this winter, and in winters to come they can be added to the holiday decorations. Each of these endearing gifts will become a family treasure.

Crocheted Baby Stockings and Mittens

**Materials for 1 pair of stockings and
   1 pair of mittens:**
fingering-weight acrylic yarn: 2 (250-yard)
   skeins white, 1 (250-yard) skein baby blue
size B crochet hook

SIZES: Stockings are 4" from heel to toe and 6¾" high. Mittens are 2¾" wide and 3¾" long.
GAUGE: 5 sc = 1".
Note: Crochet Abbreviations are on page 153.
STOCKINGS: FOOT: *Rnd 1:* With white, ch 20, 3 sc in 2nd ch from hook, sc in each of next 17 ch, 3 sc in last ch, working back along opposite side of ch, sc in each of next 17 ch = 40 sts. *Note:* Work in a spiral. Use a small safety pin to mark the beg of each rnd. *Rnd 2:* Sc in next st, 3 sc in next st, sc in each of next 19 sts, 3 sc in next st, sc in each of next 18 sts. *Rnds 3-5:* Sc in each st to center st of 3-sc group, 3 sc in center st of group, sc in each st around = 50 sts after rnd 5. (Mark center st of last 3-sc group to indicate center of toe of stocking. Move marker up with each of next 5 rnds.) *Rnds 6-10:* Sc in each st around. Fasten off after rnd 10.
INSTEP: *Note:* For rows 1-8, work back and forth in rows across 6 sts at toe. *Row 1:* Join blue with sl st in sc 3 sts before marked st, ch 1, sc in same st and each of next 5 sts, sl st in next 2 white sc, turn. *Rows 2-8:* Sc in each of next 6 blue sts, sl st in next 2 white sc, turn. *Row 9:* Sc in each of 6 blue instep sts and in each white st around stocking, join with a sl st in first sc = 34 sts. Fasten off.
LEG: *Rnds 1-25:* Join white with sl st in st at heel edge of stocking, sc in each st around. Fasten off after rnd 25. *Rnd 26:* Join blue with sl st in any st, sc in each st around. Fasten off.
CORDING: Cut 5 (2-yard) strands of blue yarn and, handling all strands as 1, knot at each end. Tuck 1 end under your foot or other stationary object. Twist other end clockwise about 200 times or until strand is tightly twisted along its entire length. Fold twisted length in half, bringing knotted ends together and maintaining tension. Knot to secure knotted ends together. Knot to secure folded end.
POM-POMS: For 1 pom-pom, hold 1 strand each of blue and white yarns together as 1 and wrap 20 times around a 1"-wide strip of cardboard. Remove yarn from cardboard and knot another piece of yarn tightly around center of bundle. Cut through loops at each end and fluff yarn to make pom-pom. Trim ends even. Repeat to make a second pom-pom.
Sew 1 pom-pom securely to each end of cording.
TOP EDGE OF STOCKING: *Rnd 1:* Join white with sl st in st at heel edge of stocking. Leaving a 4" tail, lay cording on top edge of stocking leg and dc in each st around, encasing cording in sts. Fasten off. *Rnds 2 and 3:* Join blue with sl st in any st, sc in each st around. Fasten off.
Repeat to make second stocking.
MITTENS: FINGER SECTION: *Rnd 1:* With white, ch 8, 2 sc in 2nd ch from hook, sc in each of next 5 ch, 3 sc in last ch, working back along opposite side of ch, sc in each of next 5 ch. *Note:* Work in a spiral. Use a small safety pin to mark the beg of each rnd. *Rnds 2 and 3:* * Sc in each st to center st of next 3-sc group, 3 sc in center st of group, rep from * around = 24 sts. *Rnds 4-13:* Sc in each st around. Fasten off.
THUMB: *Rnd 1:* With white, ch 5, 2 sc in 2nd ch from hook, sc in each of next 2 ch, 3 sc in last ch, working back along opposite side of ch, sc in each of next 2 ch = 10 sts. *Rnds 2-9:* Sc in each st around. *Rnd 10:* To join thumb to finger section, insert hook in first st of last rnd of finger section and work 1 sc through both pieces, sc in each st around finger section, sc in each st around thumb piece = 33 sts.

Continued on next page.

WRIST: *Rnds 1-4:* Sc in each st around. Fasten off after rnd 4. *Rnd 5:* Join blue, sc in each st around. Fasten off. *Rnds 6 and 7:* Join white, rep rnd 5. Fasten off after rnd 7. *Rnds 8 and 9:* Join blue, rep rnd 5. Fasten off after rnd 9.

Repeat for second mitten.

Referring to stocking instructions above for cording and pom-poms, make 1 length of twisted cording and 2 pom-poms. Referring to photograph on page 66 for placement, sew 1 end of cording to outside edge of each mitten at wrist. Sew 1 pom-pom over each end of cording.

Knitted Baby Stockings and Mittens

Materials for 1 pair of stockings and
1 pair of mittens:
chart and color key on page 143
fingering-weight acrylic yarn: 3 (226-yard)
  skeins off-white
size 3 knitting needles
stitch holders
tapestry needle
size 5 pearl cotton: 1 (27-yard) skein each
  light green, pink, yellow

SIZES: Stockings are 5" from heel to toe and 9" high. Mittens are 3" wide and 5" long.

GAUGE: 15 sts and 20 rows = 2" in St st.

Note: Knitting Abbreviations are on page 153. To inc: K into the front and then the back of the st.

STOCKINGS: FOOT: Cast on 29 sts. *Rows 1, 2, 4, 6, 8, and 10:* K across. *Row 3:* K 1, inc 1, k 10, inc 1, k 3, inc 1, k 10, inc 1, k 1 = 33 sts. *Row 5:* K 1, inc 1, k 11, inc 1, k 5, inc 1, k 11, inc 1, k 1 = 37 sts. *Row 7:* K 1, inc 1, k 12, inc 1, k 7, inc 1, k 12, inc 1, k 1 = 41 sts. *Row 9:* K 1, inc 1, k 13, inc 1, k 9, inc 1, k 13, inc 1, k 1 = 45 sts. *Row 11:* K 17, sl these sts onto holder, k 11, sl these sts onto 2nd holder, k 17, sl these sts onto 3rd holder. Cut yarn. Mark this row as right side.

INSTEP: Return 11 sts from 2nd holder to needle. With wrong side facing, join yarn, p across. *Rows 1-19:* Work even in St st. After row 19, cut yarn, sl sts back onto 2nd holder. Return sts from first holder to needle, return sts from 2nd holder to needle, return sts from 3rd holder to needle.

LEG: *Row 1:* With wrong side facing, join yarn, k across. *Row 2:* P across. *Rows 3-5:* K across. *Rows 6-8:* P across. *Row 9:* K across. *Row 10:* P across. *Row 11:* K 2 tog, k rem sts. *Rows 12-24:* * K 1, p 1, rep from * across. *Rows 25-27:* K across. *Rows 28-30:* P

Right: Penelope Bear's upturned nose and sweet expression will endear her to many—but most of all to the lucky little girl who will cherish Penelope as her very own.

across. *Rows 31-33:* K across. *Rows 34-36:* P across. *Rows 37-39:* K across. *Rows 40-42:* P across. *Rows 43-45:* K across. *Rows 46-48:* P across. *Rows 49-51:* K across. *Rows 52-59:* * K 1, p 1, rep from * across.

CUFF: *Rows 1, 3, 5, 7, 9, 11, 13, 15, and 17 (wrong side):* K 1, (p 2, k 1, p 2, k 10, p 2, k 1), p 2, k 2, rep between ( ) once more, p 2, k 1. *Rows 2, 4, 6, 8, 10, 12, 14, 16, and 18:* P across. After row 18, cut yarn. *Row 19:* Join pink thread, p across. *Row 20:* K across. *Row 21:* Bind off as follows: Bind off 2 sts, * inc 1, k 1, turn, p 3 sts, turn, bind off 6 sts, rep from * across, bind off last st. Fasten off.

FINISHING: Weave openings at the sides of instep. Weave seam from foot to bottom edge of cuff. Reverse seam at cuff so that seam will be hidden when cuff is turned down.

Duplicate-stitch flower on St st section of cuff according to chart and color key. For duplicate stitching, thread tapestry needle with 1 strand of pearl cotton. Starting from wrong side, bring needle up through the stitch below one to be covered, leaving a 2" tail of pearl cotton. Pass needle from right to left under stitch above the one to be covered (see Diagram 1). Reinsert needle into stitch through which you originally pulled needle (see Diagram 2).

When finished, weave yarn tail through several stitches on wrong side of fabric.

Repeat to make second stocking.

MITTENS: CUFF: Cast on 43 sts. *Rows 1-5:* K across. *Rows 6, 8, 10, 12, 14, and 16:* K 1, * p 2, k 1, p 2, k 7, rep from * twice more, p 2, k 1, p 2, k 1. *Rows 7, 9, 11, 13, 15, and 17:* P across. *Row 18:* K 2 tog, * p 1, k 1, rep from * across. *Rows 19-23:* * K 1, p 1, rep from * across. *Rows 24-31:* Work even in St st.

THUMB: *Row 1:* K 14 sts, sl these sts onto holder, k 2 tog, k 12, sl rem 15 sts onto 2nd holder (13 sts rem on needle). *Row 2:* P across. *Rows 3-11:* Work even in St st. *Row 12:* K 1, * k 2 tog, k 2, rep from * twice more (10 sts rem). Cut yarn, leaving a 10" tail. Thread tail through rem sts and pull up tightly. Weave thumb seam from tip to base with rem yarn.

FINGER SECTION: Sl 15 sts from 2nd holder onto needle. With right side facing, join yarn at base of thumb, k 2 tog, k rem 13 sts. Turn, p 14 sts on needle and 14 sts from first holder (begin purling sts from first holder at base of thumb). *Rows 1-12:* Work even in St st. *Rows 13-22:* * K 1, p 1, rep from * across. *Row 23:* P 2 tog across row (14 sts rem). Cut yarn, leaving a 12" tail. Thread tail through rem sts and pull up tightly. Weave hand seam from tip to cuff with rem yarn.

FINISHING: Referring to finishing instructions for stocking and diagrams for duplicate stitching, duplicate-stitch flower on St st section of hand according to chart and color key.

Repeat to make second mitten, working duplicate-stitched flower on opposite side of mitten (see photograph on page 66).

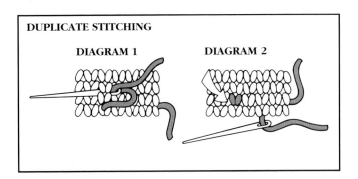

DUPLICATE STITCHING

DIAGRAM 1   DIAGRAM 2

Penelope Bear

Materials:
patterns on pages 146-47
tracing paper
⅓ yard (45"-wide) brown wool flannel
water-soluble marker
2 (¼") cream buttons
polyester stuffing
cream size 3 pearl cotton
darning needle
black embroidery floss
⅝ yard (2½"-wide) cream lace
thread to match fabric and lace
small cluster of artificial pink flowers
⅝ yard (⅜"-wide) pink velvet ribbon

Note: Patterns include ¼" seam allowances.

Using tracing paper, transfer patterns to brown flannel and cut out. Using water-soluble marker, transfer all pattern markings to flannel.

With right sides facing and raw edges aligned, stitch head front pieces together along center seam. Using brown thread, sew on buttons for eyes.

With right sides facing and raw edges aligned, stitch 2 ear pieces together, leaving open where indicated on pattern. Clip curves and turn. Repeat for other ear.

With right sides facing and raw edges aligned, baste ears to head back where indicated on pattern, easing straight edge of ear along curve of head. With *Continued on next page.*

right sides facing, raw edges aligned, and center mark on head back matching center seam on head front, stitch head front to head back, catching ears in seam and leaving head open where indicated on pattern. Clip curves and turn. Stuff firmly.

With right sides facing and raw edges aligned, stitch body front pieces together from dot to dot along center seam (see pattern). With right sides facing and raw edges aligned, stitch body front to body back, leaving open where indicated on pattern. Clip curves and turn. Stuff firmly.

Turn seam allowances under and, matching center front seams, slipstitch head to body.

With right sides facing and raw edges aligned, stitch 2 arm pieces together, leaving open where indicated on pattern. Clip curves and turn. Stuff firmly. Turn seam allowance under; slipstitch opening closed. Repeat for other arm. Align 1 arm along 1 side seam of body, with top of arm 1" below neck seam. Using 2 strands of pearl cotton, insert darning needle from outside of arm to underside at 1 of the dots indicated on pattern. Holding arm loosely against body, catch body fabric at side seam and bring needle back through arm at other dot. Pulling threads tightly, tie ends of pearl cotton into a double knot on outside of arm. Cut pearl cotton, leaving ½" ends. Repeat to attach other arm.

Using 2 strands of black embroidery floss and referring to pattern and photograph, satin-stitch nose. Without cutting floss, make a 1½"-long straightstitch along center seam line and a ¾"-long straightstitch out from center seam for each side of mouth.

Using cream thread, run a gathering thread along straight edge of lace. Pull to gather lace to fit around neck; tack ends together at center front to form a collar. Tack flowers to top of collar. Wrap ribbon around back of head and in front of ears; tie in a bow at top of head. Tack bow at center seam line.

Snow-Dusted Ornaments

Materials for 1 ornament:
metal cookie cutter in desired shape
large scrap of ½"-thick white Styrofoam
3" length of florist's wire
craft glue
paintbrushes
acrylic modeling paste
iridescent glitter
blue or pink acrylic paint

Using metal cookie cutter, cut ornament from Styrofoam. Gently finger-press edges of ornament to round and smooth edges. If desired, use point of pencil to sculpt details such as eyes and mouth.

To make a hanger, bend wire in half to form a U-shape. Apply glue to ends of wire and insert into top of ornament so that a ¼" loop extends from ornament. Let dry.

Paint ornament and hanger with several coats of modeling paste, covering entire ornament and letting dry between applications.

For white ornament, sprinkle with glitter while paste is still wet. Let dry.

For pink or blue ornament, after paste dries, paint ornament desired color. Sprinkle with glitter while paint is still wet. Let dry.

Right: Not even the baby's room should miss out on the magic of Christmas. On a special little tree, hang this twinkling host of Snow-Dusted Ornaments, created from your own collection of cookie cutters. Accent them with Gilded Walnut Baskets, which are halves of walnut shells with handles of gold braid glued inside. Each shell is coated with gold metallic paint, trimmed with lace and fancy ribbon, and lined with tissue paper and a bit of fluffy cotton.

Heirloom Silhouettes

These silhouettes portray the touching scenes of a family Christmas—children carefully hanging their stockings in anticipation of Santa's visit; daughter helping mother with the Christmas baking; and sisters lovingly exchanging homemade gifts.

The art of paper silhouetting, which began in America in the early 18th century, preceded photography as a way of depicting people realistically. To make the first paper silhouettes, the subject sat beside a candle so that the shadow of his or her profile was cast on paper attached to the wall. The artist simply traced the shadow. Since these life-size drawings were difficult to display, however, artists eventually began the freehand drawing of much smaller silhouettes.

By this time, the art of *scherenschnitte*, or cutting paper with scissors to create finely detailed scenes or designs, had been brought to America by German immigrants. Artists began using the technique of *scherenschnitte* to make their black-on-white silhouettes. You can use the same technique to create these simple scenes of Christmases past and present.

Materials for 1 silhouette:
patterns on page 145
carbon paper
1 (8" x 10") sheet of black silhouette paper
small sharp scissors
artist's spray adhesive
1 (8½" x 11") sheet of medium-weight white
  paper for background

Note: Silhouette paper is black on 1 side and white on the other, which makes it easy to transfer silhouette pattern to paper. It is important to use very sharp scissors to cut out design.

Using carbon paper, transfer pattern to white side of silhouette paper. Cut out white areas of pattern, beginning with areas closest to center of design and working outward. When cutting inner areas, use sharp, pointed end of scissors to puncture paper before cutting out area.

Spray white side of design with adhesive. Center design, black side up, on white background paper; carefully press to paper. Let dry. Frame as desired.

In the Hispanic Tradition, the Reverence of the Season Reigns

In the United States, every culture brings its unique traditions to the joyous celebration of Christmas. For Hispanic Americans, the season combines Santa Claus with the saints and Frosty the Snowman with multicolored *piñatas*. This melding of cultures grows even richer when the American Indian and Spanish influences on the season are explored.

Hispanic Catholics begin the festivities early with the Feast Day of Our Lady of Guadalupe on December 12. This feast day has a natural link with the start of Christmas, coming as it does so soon after the beginning of Advent. Just as Christmas celebrates the birth of Christ, the Feast Day of Guadalupe celebrates the birth of the knowledge of Christ in the Americas.

In the oldest Hispanic church in Houston, Our Lady of Guadalupe Church, the preparations for the *Fiesta de la Virgen de Guadalupe* begin with a novena, which is nine days of prayer, daily Mass, and sermons for the Patroness of the Americas. After the novena, the congregation readies for the colorful celebration to begin very early on the morning of December 12. By 5:00 a.m., parishioners stream into the historic church in a procession of color, music, pageantry, and devotion. The official church choir takes second place to *mariachi* bands, *matachine* dancers, and parishioners spontaneously singing *mañanitas*—birthday songs—for the birth of the Catholic religion in Mexico.

"There is a sense of reverence and informality at the same time," explains parish priest Father James Steffes. "It's not the reverence of a well-orchestrated or well-defined group, but it is a group of people who share a common faith."

One lifelong member of Our Lady of Guadalupe Church, Petra Guillen, describes the excitement very personally: "You think the whole time—it's like you're going to see your mother to wish her a happy birthday."

Right: This reverent pageant of color, music, and dance begins with a procession. The dancers carry rattles and wear jingle bells on their costumes as noisemakers. Masked figures, representing good and evil, move among the dancers.

Far right: The archway above the altar of Our Lady of Guadalupe Church in Houston reads: Reina de las Americas, *or* Queen of the Americas. *The stunning mosaic evokes the image of Our Lady of Guadalupe displayed in the Basilica in Mexico City.*

Bottom right: With trumpets and violins, this professional mariachi *band performs Spanish songs to herald the procession for the* Fiesta de Guadalupe.

Above: The adobe chapel was built to honor Our Lady of Guadalupe. The oval inset of her image is above the doorway.

Above: The Ortegas do not travel much, but their chapel draws visitors from all over the country. "We have met so many people, which has made our lives more interesting," says Eulogio.

A Chapel for Our Lady in Velarde

In ceremonies ranging from public to private, august to intimate, the Feast Day of Our Lady of Guadalupe marks the beginning of the Christmas season for many Hispanic Catholics.

An artistic couple in Velarde, New Mexico, honor Our Lady of Guadalupe in a personal way. Eulogio Ortega, a wood carver, and his wife, Zoraida, a painter and weaver, built and finely decorated an adobe chapel in the orchard beside their home. They dedicated their chapel, which glows with hand-carved and hand-painted religious imagery, to her.

"Every year in December, we have a Mass in her honor and invite all our neighbors. After the Mass, we gather in our house and have a feast," Eulogio says. "That is the highlight of Christmas for us."

Eulogio began his craft of religious folk carving when a *santo*, or a carved saintly image, of the Archangel Rafael was stolen from El Santuario de Chimayo, a local shrine. It saddened him that such a beautiful piece had been lost. He decided to carve a replica to present to the Santuario.

"I found the art of carving so absorbing and fascinating," Eulogio says, "that I kept carving different *santos*." He began duplicating *santos* that had been carved by the old *santeros*, or religious image carvers, following their method of carving, sanding, applying gesso, and then painting.

The history of *santos* carving is an interesting one. Franciscan missionaries, who were brought over with the Spanish settlers to convert the American Indians in New Mexico, encouraged the Indians to carve religious statuary for the newly constructed Catholic churches. The statues were carved out of cottonwood and ponderosa pine and painted with water-based paints made from cinnabar, iron oxide, carbon, and other native materials. The result was a mixture of traditional Indian and Hispanic forms influenced by European baroque painting techniques that had traveled north from Mexico.

"Zoraida suggested that since we had regressed to this fascinating ancient art, we should also build a chapel as in the old days," Eulogio says.

Zoraida, a weaver with a radiant sense of color, has painted almost all of Eulogio's carvings. When the chapel was built, she painted the interior.

"It is interesting that my wife painted the altar screen, because women never used to paint the altar screens," Eulogio says. "Today there are a few women even carving the *santos*. It goes to show that women are getting into every field and doing a remarkable job."

"I carved a Lady of Guadalupe for a man from Los Angeles," Eulogio says, "and I've carved many images of her for many different people. So, in a way, I help to perpetuate her image as she was conceived in the mind of the ancient *santero*."

Left: The interior of the Ortega chapel is a striking contrast of stark simplicity and exquisite detail. It took Zoraida one year to paint the altar screen, the santo *of Our Lady of Guadalupe, and the central crucifix carved by Eulogio. The* santo *on the far right is of San Ysidro, patron saint of farmers.*

Below: The altar screen portrays saintly figures and images of Mary. The images are delicately framed with crosses, flowers, and swirls.

Left: Pressed-cotton figures, such as this cat and mouse, reached the height of popularity in the 1920s. Since they weren't as fragile as the fine glass ornaments, they were placed on lower branches so that children could play with them. Consequently, the cotton creations are rare today.

Inset at right: This delicate hand-blown sailboat, known as a "fantasy piece," was made sometime between 1880 and 1907, before glass ornaments were blown into molds.

Christmas at the Gotham Book Mart

A literary jewel sparkles on West 47th Street in the diamond district of New York City. The sign above the door proclaims, "Wise Men Fish Here." Since the Gotham Book Mart opened its doors in 1920, literary giants, including Truman Capote, Tennessee Williams, D. H. Lawrence, and Eudora Welty have lured eager anglers to this spot.

The Gotham Book Mart regularly hosts opening parties for writers' new works. This tradition took an interesting turn in December 1977, after owner Andreas Brown met Phillip Snyder, author of *The Christmas Tree Book: The History of the Christmas Tree and Antique Christmas Tree Ornaments* (still available in paperback). Although Andreas had only hosted parties for "literary" books in the past, he was so charmed by *The Christmas Tree Book* that an idea struck him. He told the author that he would have a party to introduce the book if Mr. Snyder and his wife would decorate a tree in the shop with their collection.

"I was enchanted with the book," Andreas remembers. It reminded him of the time and care his family spent preparing their own tree every Christmas and the great pains taken to safely pack away each fragile ornament when the holidays were over.

The exhibit filled the shop's second-floor gallery and fascinated crowds of visitors. The following year, Andreas himself set up a Christmas tree and displayed a collection that he brought together from estate sales, flea markets, and antiques dealers from around the country.

Since then, Andreas has offered items for sale at the annual Christmas show. Some collectors, such as the Forbes Museum and the Metropolitan Museum of Art, make purchases every year. Private collectors, among them illustrator Edward Gorey, also exhibit their favorite ornaments on the Gotham tree and in glass cases that surround the upstairs room.

Andreas refers to vintage photographs as a guide for selecting ornaments and placing them on the tree. Usually only Edwardian and Victorian ornaments and other important rarities dated before 1930 are honored, although more recent surprises can sometimes be found tucked into the branches.

"Grandmothers, little children, school classes—all come in to see the exhibit," Andreas says of his annual Christmas display. "It's a good thing for the community."

Right: After months of scouring the country for the finest ornaments, it takes Andreas another week just to decorate the Gotham Book Mart's stunning turn-of-the-century-style Christmas tree. Collector and dealer Jim Morrison provides many hours of the hard work. He helps to set up the event, even bringing a fresh 12-foot tree to New York from his hometown in Maryland.

A Good Send-Off

These days, friends and loved ones are often apart at Christmas. Shipping gifts has become an essential part of sharing the spirit and preserving the traditions of the holiday. But the process doesn't have to be a frenzy of paper, boxes, and tape. With careful planning and a little organization, you can send almost any gift anywhere.

Above: Worried about bows being crushed when gifts are wrapped for mailing? Try flat wraps. You simply wrap the box in brown or tinted packaging paper; then tear or cut out colored artist's paper into desired designs and glue them into position. Glue on thin metallic cording to look like a strand of bright Christmas lights or fluffy cotton batting to complete a jolly Santa.

Guidelines for Shipping

★First, plan to have your packages ready to mail three to four weeks before Christmas, and even earlier if you are sending gifts overseas.

★To package each gift for shipping, start with a corrugated box in good condition. Select one that is large enough to allow for adequate cushioning materials on all sides of your gift.

★Once you've found a suitable container, pad the bottom with several inches of packing material. Choose the packing material that will cushion your gift the best. Suitable materials include brown paper or newspaper, shredded paper, bubble wrap, popped popcorn, or polystyrene "peanuts." (If you choose popcorn as a cushioning material, use air-popped popcorn to avoid grease stains on the gift and the shipping box.) Using several types of cushioning, such as bubble wrap and shredded paper, is most effective.

★Use enough packing material that the contents of the box do not move when you shake it. Overfill the box before you close it, shaking it once again to make sure the contents are secure. If necessary, add more packing material to keep items from shifting. Before sealing, place a duplicate address label on the inside of the box.

★Seal your box with a strong, two-inch-wide tape that is reinforced, pressure-sensitive, or water-activated. Do not use cellophane tape, masking tape, string, or twine.

★Place one clearly written address label on the top of the box, but not on a seam or on the sealing tape. Include a complete return address in the top left-hand corner of your label.

★Once you're ready to ship your package, you have a number of options. The U.S. Postal Service offers several choices, from third class mail to overnight delivery. Delivery centers also have various shipping possibilities. Privately owned mailing services are often conveniently located and, for a fee, will route your package to any of the services above. In fact, they'll even pack your gift for a small fee.

★These guidelines are to help you ship your gifts in the quickest and safest manner. However, accidents do happen and damage-free shipping cannot be guaranteed. At no or little cost, insurance is available through the postal service or shipping center. Should a package arrive with the contents broken, report the incident to the post office or shipping center at once.

Right: If shipped safely cushioned, home-baked cookies and cakes will look and taste as good on arrival as when they came out of your oven.

Shipping Breakables

Wrap each item securely in several layers of bubble wrap and secure it with strong tape. Place the gift in the center of the box and stuff additional packing material, such as shredded paper, firmly around all sides of the item.

If you are shipping more than one gift in a box, wrap each separately in bubble wrap and then in a brown paper bag. Do not pack heavy items with fragile items unless each is secure and stabilized.

The farther you keep the gifts away from each other and away from the corners and sides of the box, the less chance there is of damage.

Make sure boxes are clearly labeled "Fragile," so that shippers will know to handle them with care.

Shipping Food

Keep your Christmas cookies and cakes from arriving in crumbs by adding extra cushioning to their containers.

Line each container with waxed paper or aluminum foil and add your favorite baked goodies. Stuff the container with additional waxed paper before closing. Gently shake the container. If you can hear the contents shifting, add more paper. Repeat the process until the contents are secure.

Label the box "Perishables," so that the recipient will know that the box should be opened right away.

Shipping Greenery

Whether it's a swag of evergreen garland woven with clusters of pinecones or a simple bundle of holly tied with a bright red bow, a faraway friend will delight in a box of freshly cut holiday greenery.

To send a gift of the fresh outdoors, select and cut a hearty bunch of greenery; be sure to include any berries, nuts, pinecones, or seed pods that accompany the leaves. Lightly spray the leaves with a very fine mist of water. Place the greenery in a loose plastic bag, but do not seal it closed.

Choose a box that is a little larger than the cutting and pad the bottom with one or two inches of packing material. (Shredded paper works well.) Place the bagged greenery in the box and overfill it with additional shredded paper before sealing the box.

Send your cuttings via a two-day shipping service so that they will arrive fresh and green. Again, mark the box "Perishables," so that the recipient will open it right away.

Note: In general, plants and greenery are mailable within the United States. However, plant quarantines may apply to certain states. Contact your local post office for applicable shipping regulations.

A Country Christmas Pantry

HEARTY HOLIDAY BRUNCH

CROSS-STITCH FOR THE KITCHEN

SPICE UP GIFT-GIVING

SWEETS TO SHARE

FAUX FRUIT FOR A WINTER'S TABLE

IDEAS: QUICK CANAPÉS

Above: Pastry-wrapped Parmesan-Sausage Strudel packages wait for the festivities to begin. Hot Curried Fruit and Walnut-Blueberry Streusel Cake offer contrast and complement.

Hearty Holiday Brunch

For a warming, nutritious holiday brunch, individual timbales, strudels, and empanadas will hit the spot. Flaky pastry and flavorful filling make a delicious meal in themselves. Hot Curried Fruit adds a spicy-sweet accent. Close with an ample slice of Walnut-Blueberry Streusel Cake for complete contentment.

82

Parmesan-Sausage Strudel

½ pound mild Italian sausage
1 medium onion, chopped
1 medium sweet red pepper, chopped
2 tablespoons all-purpose flour
⅓ cup sour cream
6 eggs, lightly beaten
½ cup plus 2 tablespoons grated Parmesan
   cheese, divided
2 tablespoons butter or margarine
30 sheets frozen phyllo pastry, thawed and
   divided
1 cup butter or margarine, melted

Cook sausage in a large skillet until browned, stirring to crumble. Remove sausage, reserving drippings in skillet, and drain on paper towels. Sauté onion and pepper in drippings until tender; drain well. Combine sausage and sautéed onion mixture in a medium bowl. Sprinkle with flour and stir well. Stir in sour cream; set aside.

Combine eggs and ¼ cup of cheese, beating with a wire whisk until blended. Melt 2 tablespoons butter in a large skillet. Add egg mixture and cook, without stirring, until mixture begins to set on bottom. Draw a spatula across bottom of pan to form large curds. Gently stir in sausage mixture. Continue cooking until eggs are thickened but still moist, stirring only occasionally. Remove from heat and set aside.

Place 1 sheet of phyllo on a flat surface. (Keep remaining phyllo covered with a slightly damp towel.) Lightly brush phyllo with melted butter. Layer 2 more sheets of phyllo on first sheet, brushing each sheet with butter. Sprinkle with 1 tablespoon cheese. Spoon about ¾ cup egg mixture onto 1 short edge of layered phyllo. Spread mixture to form a rectangle that is centered between long edges of phyllo and 3" from short edge. Fold nearest short edge, then long edges, of phyllo over egg mixture; then roll jelly-roll fashion. Place seam side down on an ungreased baking sheet.

To make ribbon, cut 1 sheet of phyllo in half crosswise and brush both halves with butter. Fold each half lengthwise to form a 1" strip. Wrap strips at right angles around phyllo package; trim excess phyllo. Brush with butter.

To make bow, cut another sheet of phyllo in half crosswise and brush with butter. Fold 1 half lengthwise to form a 1" strip; brush with butter. Fold strip in half to form a 1" loop with tails. Holding the strip at the base of the loop, fold tails to make 2 smaller loops on each side. Arrange bow on phyllo package. Cover phyllo package with a slightly damp towel.

Repeat procedure 5 more times with remaining phyllo, butter, Parmesan cheese, and egg mixture.

Bake, uncovered, at 375° for 15 minutes or until lightly browned. Yield: 6 servings.

Beef-and-Pepper Empanadas

2 slices bacon
¾ pound boneless sirloin steak, cut into ½"
   cubes
½ cup chopped onion
¼ cup chopped green pepper
¼ cup chopped sweet red pepper
1 clove garlic, minced
¼ cup plus 2 tablespoons canned diluted beef
   broth
2 teaspoons chili powder
1 teaspoon dried whole oregano
½ teaspoon salt
⅛ teaspoon ground red pepper
½ cup frozen whole kernel corn, thawed
¼ cup plus 1 tablespoon tomato paste
Pastry for double-crust 9" pie, divided

Cook bacon in a large skillet until crisp; remove bacon, reserving drippings in skillet. Crumble bacon and set aside.

Add sirloin to drippings and cook until meat is browned on all sides. Remove meat with a slotted spoon. Add onion, peppers, and garlic, and sauté until tender. Stir in reserved bacon, sirloin, broth, chili powder, oregano, salt, and red pepper; bring to a boil. Cover, reduce heat, and simmer 45 minutes or until beef is tender, stirring occasionally.

Stir in corn and tomato paste. Cook, uncovered, 5 minutes or until thickened.

Divide pastry into 8 equal portions. Roll each of 6 portions into a 7" circle. Spoon about ⅓ cup of meat mixture onto each circle; moisten edges of dough with water. Fold each circle in half; press edges together with a fork. Transfer empanadas to an ungreased baking sheet. Flute edges, if desired.

Roll remaining pastry to ⅛" thickness. Using a sharp knife, cut decorative designs from pastry. Dampen 1 side of each cutout with water. Arrange cutouts, dampened sides down, as desired on top of empanadas.

Bake at 400° for 20 minutes or until browned. Yield: 6 servings.

Chicken-and-Mushroom Pie

1 (3½- to 4-pound) whole chicken
1¼ teaspoons salt, divided
1¼ teaspoons pepper, divided
1 cup peeled, diced potato
¼ cup plus 2 tablespoons butter or
    margarine, divided
1½ cups sliced fresh mushrooms
1 cup sliced celery
1 cup diced carrot
2½ tablespoons all-purpose flour
¾ cup milk
1 teaspoon dried whole thyme
¼ teaspoon dried whole basil
1 cup frozen English peas, thawed
½ (17¼-ounce) package frozen commercial
    puff pastry, thawed

Place chicken in a Dutch oven and cover with water. Add 1 teaspoon salt and 1 teaspoon pepper; bring to a boil. Cover, reduce heat, and simmer 1 hour or until chicken is tender. Drain chicken, reserving 1½ cups broth. Bone and chop chicken; set aside.

Place reserved broth in a small saucepan, and cook over high heat until reduced to ¾ cup. Set aside.

Boil potato 15 minutes or until tender; drain and set aside.

Melt 3 tablespoons butter in a large skillet over low heat; add mushrooms, celery, and carrot, and sauté until tender.

Melt remaining butter in heavy saucepan over low heat; add flour, stirring until smooth. Cook 1 minute, stirring constantly. Gradually add reserved broth and milk; cook over medium heat, stirring constantly, until mixture is thickened and bubbly. Stir in thyme, basil, and remaining ¼ teaspoon salt and pepper.

Combine sauce, chicken, and mushroom mixture in a large bowl; stir in peas. Spoon into a buttered 1½-quart casserole. On a floured surface, roll pastry to ⅛" thickness. Cut a circle of pastry 1" larger than top rim of casserole. (Reserve any remaining pastry to make decorative designs for top of pie, if desired.) Place pastry over dish, folding edges under and pressing firmly on rim to seal. Place decorative designs on top, if desired. Bake at 400° for 20 to 25 minutes or until golden brown. Let stand 10 minutes before serving. Yield: 6 servings.

Spinach-and-Cheese Timbale

1 (10-ounce) package frozen chopped
    spinach, thawed
½ cup chopped leek or onion
½ cup shredded carrot
2 teaspoons vegetable oil
1 cup (4 ounces) shredded Gruyère cheese
1 cup (4 ounces) shredded mozzarella cheese
3 tablespoons all-purpose flour
4 eggs, lightly beaten
½ cup milk
½ cup ricotta cheese
¼ teaspoon salt
¼ teaspoon dried whole thyme
¼ teaspoon dried whole rosemary, crushed
⅛ teaspoon pepper
Dash of ground red pepper
16 sheets frozen phyllo pastry, thawed
½ cup butter or margarine, melted
Garnishes: leek strips and carrot curls

Drain spinach well, pressing between paper towels until barely moist.

Sauté leek and carrot in oil in a large skillet until tender. Remove from heat and stir in spinach; set aside.

Combine Gruyère and mozzarella cheeses and flour in a large bowl; toss well.

Combine eggs and next 7 ingredients in a large bowl; stir in reserved spinach mixture. Add cheese mixture and stir until well blended. Set aside.

Place 1 sheet of phyllo on a flat surface. (Keep remaining phyllo covered with a slightly damp towel.) Lightly brush phyllo with melted butter. Top with another sheet of phyllo and brush with butter. Fold layered phyllo in half lengthwise; fold in half again. Place 1 end of phyllo strip in center of a lightly greased 1-quart souffle dish. Press strip along bottom and up the side of souffle dish, allowing excess to hang over edge of dish.

Repeat procedure 3 more times, placing strips so that they divide dish into fourths. Repeat procedure 4 more times, placing 1 strip each between adjacent strips, so that dish is completely lined. Pour spinach mixture into prepared dish. Fold ends of strips over top of spinach mixture, overlapping ends at center. Brush with butter. Bake at 350° for 35 minutes or until timbale is golden. Cool on a wire rack 15 minutes. Carefully invert timbale onto a serving platter. Garnish, if desired. Yield: 6 servings.

Walnut-Blueberry Streusel Cake

2¼ cups all-purpose flour, divided
¼ cup firmly packed brown sugar
½ teaspoon ground cinnamon
3 tablespoons butter or margarine
⅓ cup chopped walnuts
⅓ cup butter or margarine, softened
⅔ cup sugar
1 (8-ounce) carton sour cream
2 eggs
2 teaspoons baking powder
½ teaspoon baking soda
¼ teaspoon salt
¾ teaspoon vanilla extract
2 cups fresh or frozen blueberries

Combine ½ cup flour, brown sugar, and cinnamon; cut in 3 tablespoons butter with a pastry blender until mixture resembles coarse meal. Stir in walnuts and set aside.

Beat ⅓ cup butter at medium speed of an electric mixer; gradually add sugar, beating well. Add sour cream and eggs, beating well. In a separate bowl, combine remaining 1¾ cups flour and next 3 ingredients; stir well. Add to creamed mixture; beat at medium speed of an electric mixer 5 minutes. Stir in vanilla.

Spoon batter into a greased 9" springform pan. Sprinkle blueberries over batter; top with reserved walnut mixture.

Bake at 350° for 1 hour or until a wooden pick inserted in center comes out clean. Cool in pan 15 minutes. Remove sides of springform pan. Serve warm or at room temperature. Yield: 1 (9") cake.

Hot Curried Fruit

1 (8-ounce) can sliced pineapple in juice, undrained
⅓ cup firmly packed brown sugar
1 tablespoon frozen orange juice concentrate, thawed and undiluted
¾ teaspoon curry powder
⅛ teaspoon ground cinnamon
2 small baking apples, cored
1 (16-ounce) can peach slices, drained
1 cup seedless red grapes

Drain pineapple, reserving juice. Quarter pineapple slices and set aside. Combine juice, brown sugar, and next 3 ingredients; set aside.

Slice apples crosswise into ¼" slices. Place apples, reserved pineapple, peaches, and grapes in a 1½-quart baking dish; pour reserved juice mixture over fruit. Cover and bake at 350° for 35 minutes or until apples are tender. Serve warm. Yield: 6 servings.

Right: Decorated with a sprig of holly pastry, Beef-and-Pepper Empanadas make a wonderfully filling entrée for cold and hungry guests at a winter brunch.

Cross-Stitch for the Kitchen

*Delight your favorite holiday hostess with this apron and matching bread cloth,
a set made festive by sprightly sprigs of bright-red cross-stitched cranberries.
The bread cloth can be personalized with an initial, and the apron,
with its simple repeated cross-stitch designs, is a cinch to complete.*

Hostess Apron

Materials:
charts and color key on page 148
**11½" square of 14-count maize yellow Aida
  cloth**
**11" x 7½" piece of 14-count maize yellow Aida
  cloth**
embroidery floss (see color key)
⅓ yard (45"-wide) seafoam green miniprint
2 yards (45"-wide) unbleached muslin
**1¼ yards (2"-wide) preruffled cotton ecru
  eyelet**
thread to match fabrics
2 yards (1"-wide) cranberry grosgrain ribbon

Note: Unless otherwise indicated, all seam allowances are ¼".

For bib, using 2 strands of floss and referring to chart, begin stitching design on 11½" square of Aida cloth so that left and top edges of design are 3" from left and top edges of fabric. Referring to photograph, repeat design 3 times to form a design of 4 squares. With design centered, trim finished cross-stitched piece to measure 7½" square.

For pocket border design, using 2 strands of floss and referring to chart, begin stitching design on remaining piece of Aida cloth so that left and top edges of design are 3" from left and top edges of fabric. Referring to photograph, repeat design 3 times to form a rectangle. With design centered, trim finished cross-stitched piece to measure 6¾" x 3".

From miniprint, cut the following: 2 (1¼" x 7½") and 2 (1¼" x 9") strips for bib border, 3 (3" x 36") strips for sash and insert at skirt bottom, and 2 (1¼" x 6¾") strips for pocket.

From muslin, cut the following: 1 (36") square for skirt, 1 (9") square for bib back, and 1 (6¾" x 8¾") piece for pocket.

For bib borders, with right sides facing and raw edges aligned, stitch 1 (1¼" x 7½") miniprint strip to top of cross-stitched bib design; repeat for bottom

of bib. Stitch 1 (1¼" x 9") strip to each side in same manner. Press seams toward borders.

For bib ruffle, make a 67" (4"-wide) continuous bias strip from remaining muslin. With wrong sides facing and raw edges aligned, fold strip in half lengthwise. Press. Run a gathering thread along long raw edge. Pull to gather. With raw edges aligned, baste muslin ruffle to eyelet, adjusting ruffle as needed to match eyelet length. With right sides facing and raw edges aligned, pin muslin/eyelet ruffle to miniprint borders and baste.

To make bib, with right sides facing, raw edges aligned, and ruffle toward center, stitch bib front to back, rounding corners slightly and leaving a 6" opening at bottom of bib for turning. Clip corners and turn. Slipstitch opening closed. Mark center of bottom edge of bib and press bib.

For skirt, mark 1 edge of 36" square of muslin as skirt top. Turn bottom of square under ¼" and then 2¼" and hem. Press. To prepare for insertion of ribbon band, cut all the way across skirt 6" from hem bottom. For insert, cut a 36" piece of cranberry ribbon, center along 1 (3" x 36") miniprint strip, and, using cranberry thread, topstitch ribbon in place. With right sides facing and raw edges aligned, stitch 1 long edge of insert to raw edge of skirt. With right sides facing and raw edges aligned, stitch remaining long edge of insert to raw edge of hemmed piece of skirt. Press seam toward insert. Finish sides of skirt with a narrow hem.

For pocket, with right sides facing and raw edges aligned, stitch 1 (1¼" x 6¾") miniprint strip each to the top and bottom of cross-stitched pocket border design. Press seams toward miniprint borders. With right sides facing and raw edges aligned, stitch long edge of top border to 1 short edge of muslin pocket. Trim seam and press. Turn raw edge of bottom border under ¼". Topstitch borders to pocket, ⅛" inside each long edge of top and bottom of borders. Turn side and bottom edges of pocket under ½" and press. Referring to photograph, position pocket on
Continued on page 88.

Continued on page 88.

right side of skirt. Topstitch sides and bottom of pocket to skirt, stitching ¼" from edges.

Mark center of skirt top; then run a gathering thread across skirt top and pull to measure 19". Secure thread.

For waistband sash, with right sides facing, stitch ends of remaining 2 (3" x 36") miniprint strips together to make a 72" strip. With right sides facing, raw edges aligned, and centers matching, stitch sash to skirt top. Fold sash over skirt top, turn raw edge under ¼", and slipstitch to skirt back along seam line to make waistband. To finish sash, stitch a narrow hem along all raw edges.

To join bib to skirt, center bib on waistband and slipstitch top of waistband to back of bib along bottom seam line of bib.

For neck ties, cut remaining ribbon in half. Turn 1 end of each ribbon under ¼" and slipstitch to bib back at top corners. Cut remaining ends of ribbons diagonally to prevent raveling.

Bread Cloth

Materials:
chart and color key on page 148
embroidery floss (see color key)
18" square of 20-count cream Kali cloth
thread to match fabric
tweezers

Using about 15 stitches per inch, machine-stitch ¾" inside all edges of cloth. To make fringe, use tweezers to remove all parallel threads outside machine stitching.

For decorative detail, use tweezers to remove eighth parallel thread inside machine stitching on each side.

Referring to photograph and chart and using 2 strands of floss, position and stitch design in 1 corner of bread cloth. Using 3 strands of floss, work desired letter in center of circle, using heavy black dot on both graphs to center letter.

Left: This cross-stitched initial encircled by cranberry sprigs embellishes a creamy-soft bread cloth. This motif could also spruce up a matching set of napkins.

Spice Up Gift-Giving

*Spice mixes have a myriad of uses. Try adding Chinese Spice Mix
to liquid before cooking rice. Or sprinkle Mexican Spice Mix over strips of
chicken, beef, or pork before you sauté them. Blend Italian Spice Mix
with melted butter and toss with hot popcorn. Or add Indian Spice Mix to equal
parts of sour cream and mayonnaise for a distinctive vegetable dip.*

Indian Spice Mix

⅓ cup curry powder
2 tablespoons ground cumin
1 tablespoon ground turmeric
2 teaspoons grated lemon rind
¼ teaspoon ground cinnamon
⅛ teaspoon ground cloves

   Combine all ingredients, stirring well. Store spice
mixture in an airtight container. Yield: ⅔ cup.

Mexican Spice Mix

½ cup chili powder
¼ cup paprika
2 tablespoons ground cumin
2 teaspoons garlic powder
1 teaspoon ground red pepper
1 teaspoon salt

   Combine all ingredients, stirring well. Store spice
mixture in an airtight container. Yield: 1 cup.

Italian Spice Mix

⅓ cup dried whole oregano
¼ cup dried whole basil
¼ cup dried parsley flakes
3 tablespoons rubbed sage
1 tablespoon garlic powder
1 teaspoon dried whole rosemary
1 teaspoon salt

   Combine all ingredients, stirring well. Store spice
mixture in an airtight container. Yield: 1 cup.

Chinese Spice Mix

½ cup toasted sesame seeds
3 tablespoons Chinese five-spice powder
2 tablespoons brown sugar
1 teaspoon grated orange rind
1 teaspoon salt

   Combine all ingredients, stirring well. Store spice
mixture in an airtight container. Yield: 1 cup.
   Note: Mixes can be stored for up to 3 months.
For longer storage, freeze them for up to 1 year.

Sweets to Share

*Have you ever made a gift so scrumptious
that you wished you could
keep some for yourself, too? These
recipes have generous yields, so you can
give and receive.*

Crunchy Peanut-Butter Truffles

5 ounces white chocolate, divided
⅔ cup creamy peanut butter
½ cup sifted powdered sugar
1 tablespoon vanilla extract
**⅔ cup 100% natural cereal with oats and
honey, crushed**
8 ounces semisweet chocolate, chopped
2 tablespoons shortening

Place 3 ounces white chocolate in top of a double
boiler; bring water to a boil. Reduce heat to low;
cook until chocolate melts, stirring frequently. Remove from heat and cool. Add peanut butter; beat at
low speed of an electric mixer until smooth. Add
powdered sugar and vanilla; mix well. Stir in cereal.
(Mixture will be very thick.) Shape into 1" balls and
set aside.

Place semisweet chocolate and shortening in top
of a double boiler; bring water to a boil. Reduce
heat to low; cook until chocolate melts and mixture
is smooth, stirring frequently. Dip each peanut-butter ball in melted chocolate, coating well. Place balls
on a wire rack over waxed paper. Chill 15 minutes
or until firm.

Place remaining white chocolate in top of a double boiler; bring water to a boil. Reduce heat to low;
cook until chocolate melts, stirring frequently.

*Left: With treats this mouth-watering, better make a batch to
give and one to keep on hand for well-deserved snacking.
Clockwise from top, Pistachio-Cherry Fudge Rolls, Coconut-
Cashew Crunch, Amaretto Rosettes, Crunchy Peanut-Butter
Truffles, and Mocha Meltaway Bites. (See page 93 for in-
structions on how to decorate candy gift boxes.)*

Remove from heat and cool slightly. Spoon melted chocolate into a zip-top plastic bag; remove air
and seal plastic bag. (A decorating bag fitted with a
No. 2 round tip can also be used.) Snip a tiny hole in
1 corner of zip-top bag and pipe chocolate mixture
in a decorative design over balls. Chill chocolate
balls 5 to 10 minutes or until white chocolate is
firm. Store in refrigerator in an airtight container.
Yield: 2 dozen.

Mocha Meltaway Bites

Vegetable cooking spray
3½ cups butter-flavored cookie crumbs
⅔ cup chocolate-coated coffee beans
½ cup butter or margarine, melted
2 tablespoons instant coffee granules
2 tablespoons milk
1 cup butter or margarine, softened
5 cups sifted powdered sugar, divided
1 teaspoon vanilla extract
**1 (6-ounce) package semisweet chocolate
morsels**
3 tablespoons butter or margarine

Line a 13" x 9" x 2" baking pan with aluminum
foil, allowing foil to extend 2" beyond ends of pan.
Coat foil with cooking spray; set aside.

Position knife blade in food processor bowl. Add
cookie crumbs and chocolate-coated coffee beans;
process 20 seconds or until beans are finely chopped. Transfer mixture to a medium bowl. Stir in
melted butter. Firmly press crumb mixture in bottom of prepared pan. Bake at 325° for 6 minutes.
Cool.

Dissolve instant coffee granules in milk; set aside.

Beat 1 cup butter at medium speed of an electric
mixer; gradually add 3 cups sugar, beating well. Add
coffee mixture and vanilla, beating well. Add remaining 2 cups sugar; beat until mixture is smooth.
Spread over crust; freeze until firm.

Combine chocolate morsels and 3 tablespoons
butter in top of a double boiler; bring water to a
boil. Reduce heat to low; cook until chocolate and
butter melt, stirring frequently. Spread chocolate
mixture over coffee mixture; chill 15 minutes or until chocolate is set.

Using extended pieces of foil as handles, lift layered confection out of pan and transfer to a cutting
board. Remove and discard foil. Cut confection into
1" squares. Store in refrigerator in an airtight container. Yield: About 10 dozen.

Coconut-Cashew Crunch

2 cups sugar
1 cup light corn syrup
¾ cup water
1 cup lightly salted, roasted cashews
1 cup unsweetened shredded coconut
1½ tablespoons butter or margarine
1 teaspoon baking soda
1 teaspoon vanilla extract
¼ teaspoon salt

Butter a 15" x 10" x 1" jelly-roll pan; set aside.
Combine first 3 ingredients in a large saucepan.
Cook over medium-low heat, stirring constantly, until sugar dissolves. Cover and cook over medium heat 3 minutes to wash down sugar crystals from sides of pan. Uncover and cook, stirring occasionally, until mixture reaches hard crack stage (300°). Remove from heat. Stir in cashews and remaining ingredients.

Working rapidly, pour mixture into prepared pan; spread into a thin layer. Cool completely. Break into pieces and store in an airtight container. Yield: 1¾ pounds.

Pistachio-Cherry Fudge Rolls

1½ pounds white chocolate, chopped
1 (14-ounce) can sweetened condensed milk
2 cups finely chopped pistachios, divided
1 cup chopped red and green candied
   cherries
1 teaspoon vanilla extract
⅛ teaspoon salt

Combine chocolate and milk in top of double boiler; bring water to a boil. Reduce heat to low; cook until chocolate melts and mixture is smooth, stirring frequently. Stir in ½ cup chopped pistachios, candied cherries, vanilla, and salt.

Spread fudge evenly in a waxed paper-lined 8"-square pan. Chill 1½ hours or until fudge is almost firm. Invert and remove pan. Peel off waxed paper. Cut into 4 (8" x 2") strips. Stretch and shape each strip into a 10" log; roll in remaining pistachios, pressing nuts firmly into fudge. Chill 2 hours or until firm. Cut logs into ½" slices. Store in refrigerator in an airtight container. Yield: 80 pieces.

Amaretto Rosettes

½ cup all-purpose flour
½ cup milk
1 egg, lightly beaten
1 tablespoon amaretto
2 teaspoons sugar
Vegetable oil
Powdered sugar

Combine first 5 ingredients in a medium bowl; beat at low speed of an electric mixer until blended. Cover and let stand 5 minutes.

Pour about 2" of vegetable oil in a large skillet or saucepan; heat oil to 375°. Submerge rosette end of rosette iron in hot oil and heat about 1 minute. Lift iron out of oil, allowing excess oil to drain. Dip iron into batter, being careful not to coat top of iron with batter.

Now submerge iron in hot oil. As soon as rosette is set (about 5 to 8 seconds), move iron slowly up and down to release rosette. (If necessary, pry rosette gently with a fork to release.) Fry until golden, turning once. Drain on paper towels. Repeat procedure with remaining batter.

Dust rosettes with powdered sugar. Yield: 2 dozen.
Note: Various shapes may be purchased to use with the rosette iron. The photograph on page 90 shows an angel and a flower, or rosette, shape.

Caramel-Pecan Bonbons

1¼ cups coarsely chopped pecans, toasted
3 tablespoons brown sugar
3 ounces dried apples
1 tablespoon butter or margarine, melted
1 tablespoon light corn syrup
1 teaspoon ground cinnamon
¼ teaspoon ground ginger
1 (14-ounce) package individually wrapped
   caramel candies, unwrapped
3 tablespoons whipping cream
1 tablespoon butter or margarine
1½ cups finely chopped pecans, toasted

Position knife blade in food processor bowl. Add coarsely chopped pecans and brown sugar; process until nuts are ground. Set aside. Place dried apples in food processor bowl; process until finely chopped. Combine ground pecans, apples, melted butter, corn syrup, cinnamon, and ginger, stirring well. Shape into ¾" balls and chill until firm.

Combine caramels, whipping cream, and butter in top of a double boiler; bring water to a boil. Reduce heat to low; cook until caramels and butter melt, stirring frequently. Dip each pecan ball in caramel mixture, coating well. Roll in finely chopped pecans and place on waxed paper. Let stand at room temperature until hardened. Yield: About 4 dozen.

Winter Wedding Cookies

¾ cup butter or margarine, softened
½ cup sifted powdered sugar
2 tablespoons honey
1 teaspoon vanilla extract
2 cups all-purpose flour
¼ teaspoon salt
½ cup finely chopped walnuts
Additional powdered sugar

Beat butter at medium speed of an electric mixer until light and fluffy; add ½ cup powdered sugar and honey, beating well. Stir in vanilla. Combine flour and salt; add to creamed mixture, mixing until well blended. Stir in walnuts.

Shape dough into 1" balls and place 2" apart on lightly greased cookie sheets. Bake at 325° for 12 minutes or until lightly browned. Cool slightly on cookie sheets. Roll warm cookies in additional sugar and cool on wire racks. Yield: 3 dozen.

Very Berry Valley Cookies

¾ cup butter or margarine, softened
½ cup sugar
1 egg
2 cups all-purpose flour
½ teaspoon baking powder
1 teaspoon vanilla extract
2 tablespoons semisweet chocolate
    minimorsels
3 tablespoons red raspberry preserves

Beat butter at medium speed of an electric mixer until light and fluffy; gradually add sugar, beating well. Add egg, beating well. Combine flour and baking powder; add to creamed mixture, mixing well. Stir in vanilla. Wrap dough in plastic wrap and chill 1 hour.

Divide dough in half. Shape each half into a 12" log. Place logs 4" apart on greased cookie sheet. Place the handle of a wooden spoon lengthwise down the center of each log and press gently to form a ½" indentation or "valley." Sprinkle minimorsels in indentation and spoon preserves over minimorsels. Bake at 350° for 18 minutes or until lightly browned. Cool 10 minutes on cookie sheet. Cut rolls diagonally into 1" slices and cool on wire racks. Yield: 2 dozen.

Gift Wrap with Panache

What better way to share your delectable sweets than in boxes you've decorated yourself? All you need are an assortment of boxes, bright-colored acrylic paints, and a few pieces of festive ribbon. Just a little of your time will create charming containers that will remind the recipient of you long after the holidays are gone.

While any cardboard box will work, white boxes will keep bright paints vivid. To start, use a sponge brush to paint the outside of the box with acrylic paint in the desired color. Let it dry for 20 minutes.

You can create an elegant marble effect by sponging on one or two contrasting colors with small, torn pieces of sponge. (Refer to the photograph on page 90.) Let the first color dry completely before adding a second color. Finally, add decorative details with a small paintbrush, if desired.

A variety of paintbrushes will give other boxes a personality all their own. Before painting, lightly draw your desired design onto the box with a sharp pencil. Use a small paintbrush for fine lines and tiny details and a large one for broad and dramatic strokes. Remember to let the paint dry completely before adding the next color.

After the paint is completely dry, lightly spray the box with a clear acrylic glaze and let it dry. Your gift box is now ready to be lined with a small piece of tissue paper and filled with your favorite sweets to share. Then add the final touch: a satin, metallic, or glitter-edged ribbon tied into a festive bow.

Faux Fruit for a Winter's Table

*Even a novice can master the simple technique of using
Petal Porcelain to transform inexpensive plastic fruit into
elegant decorations for the holiday setting.*

*Above: These napkin rings and candle holder dress a holiday
table with classic elegance. Old favorites from your linen chest
and a simple arrangement of poinsettias embellish the setting.
(For tips on decorating with poinsettias, see page 28.)*

Materials for both projects:
Petal Porcelain Setting Agent
white flat spray paint
acrylic paints: light green, dark green, yellow,
   cream, blue, purple, brown, holiday red
small flat paintbrush
small paintbrush with pointed tip
clear acrylic glaze spray

Candle Holder

Materials for 1 candle holder:
15 polyester "silk" leaves, assorted sizes
2"-tall wooden candle holder
assorted miniature plastic fruit
1¼ yards (⅛"-wide) ribbon

Dip 1 leaf into Petal Porcelain Setting Agent. Use
fingers to strip excess solution from leaf and arrange
wet leaf on candle holder as desired, shaping as necessary. (Solution stiffens pliable materials and acts as
a glue, immediately adhering leaves to candle holder.) Repeat with remaining leaves and fruit. Let dry.

Cut ribbon into 3 equal lengths. Dip 1 ribbon in
solution and strip excess as above. Form 3 (1") loops
and arrange on candle holder, tucking ribbon behind fruit and then curling and draping ribbon ends
over fruit and leaves. Repeat with remaining ribbons. Let dry overnight.

Following manufacturer's instructions, spray entire surface of candle holder with 1 coat of spray
paint. Let dry.

Mix together a small amount of light green and
dark green paint. Using flat paintbrush, apply paint

Right: Not only is Petal Porcelain easy to work with, it's versatile, too. To make this bread basket, for example, you use the same techniques and materials as described for the candle holder and napkin rings. The only difference: you use a basket as the base.

Petal Porcelain Tips

Use polyester "silk" leaves, not rubberized or plastic ones. The Petal Porcelain solution does not adhere well to thin, pliable objects made of rubber or plastic, and over time the paint will chip and peel. For the same reason, choose miniature fruit made of hard, nonpliable plastic.

To prevent fingers from becoming too tacky and sticking to the project, occasionally wash your hands with soap and water throughout the dipping process.

If your fingers do stick to the project, dip the handle of a paintbrush in water and hold it against the project, beside your fingers. The water will unstick your fingers, while the brush handle will help to keep the object firmly in place.

For leaves and ribbons that are difficult to manipulate, use hat pins to secure them while they dry. After dipped objects have dried, check for runs or drips before spray painting with base coat. If any have occurred, use a hair dryer to blow warm air on them for a few seconds. When the heat softens the drips, gently pick them off.

Use acrylic paints in muted or antiqued colors, as well as a light coat of clear glaze, to achieve the most realistic and satisfying painted finishes.

---

evenly over leaves. Immediately wipe gently with a paper towel, allowing leaf crevices to stay darker than flat surfaces and tips of leaves. Let dry.

Referring to photograph and using flat paintbrush, paint fruit and ribbons as desired with remaining colors of paints. If necessary, give red fruit a second coat. Let dry.

Add darker colors to accent edges of leaves and in crevices of fruit, using pointed-tip paintbrush for hard-to-reach places. Let dry.

Following manufacturer's instructions, lightly spray entire surface of candle holder with 1 coat of clear glaze. Let dry.

Napkin Rings

Materials for 4 napkin rings:
4 napkin rings with 1¼" x 3¾" bases, made of either unglazed ceramic bisque or wooden rings glued to wooden bases with wood glue
20 polyester "silk" leaves, assorted sizes
assorted miniature plastic fruit
1½ yards (⅛"-wide) ribbon

Cut ribbon into 4 equal lengths. Referring to instructions for candle holder, dip decorative items in solution and attach to napkin rings/bases. Let dry; then paint as desired. Apply glaze as above.

Farm Animal Pot Holders

*These animated pot holders are straight off the farm.
And, with their quick-to-stencil borders and fused-on appliqués,
they couldn't be easier to make.*

Materials for 1 pot holder:
patterns on page 149
tracing paper
paper-backed fusible web
**scrap of light brown cotton print for animal
    shape**
**scraps of cotton fabric for background or
    accents: green for goat, red for pig, blue for
    cow, yellow and red for rooster**
2 (10½" x 9") pieces of white cotton fabric
small sponge
black acrylic fabric paint
white sewing thread
1 (10½" x 9") piece of thick quilt batting
white quilting thread

Note: All seam allowances are ¼".
Trace pattern for animal appliqué shape onto
tracing paper. For goat, also trace pattern for grass.
For rooster, also trace patterns for feet, beak, and
comb/wattle.

Following manufacturer's instructions, fuse web
to wrong side of all fabric scraps. (Do not fuse web
to white cotton pieces.) Trace appliqué shape(s) onto
paper side of web and cut out. For pig or cow, also
cut a 5⅜" x 3⅝" rectangle for background. Set aside.

For checkerboard border, mark a 5⅜" x 3⅝" rectangle in center of 1 white cotton piece. Lightly mark
a 2- or 3-row checkerboard border around rectangle,
with each square of border measuring ½" to 1". From
sponge, cut a square the same size as squares in border. Dip 1 side of sponge square in small amount of
paint, and, referring to photograph for placement,
sponge-paint border. Let dry; then set with a hot,
dry iron.

Peel paper backing from appliqué shapes. For
goat, pig, or cow, refer to photograph for placement
and fuse grass or background in place.

Center animal appliqué shape inside stenciled
border; fuse in place. For rooster, fuse feet, beak, and
comb/wattle shapes where indicated on pattern.

Stack batting, top (right side up), and remaining
piece of white cotton fabric. Stitch, leaving an opening for turning. Clip corners, trim batting from seam
allowance, and turn. Slipstitch opening closed.

Using quilting thread, hand-quilt inside edge of
stenciled border. Repeat around outside edge of
stenciled border.

Stuffings and Dressings—An American Tradition

Of course, the most traditional dressing is usually the one your mother made. Here are tried-and-true choices with four regional accents— Northern Yankee Stuffing, Southern Sausage-Cornbread Dressing, Southwestern Chorizo-and-Corn Dressing, and Midwestern Traditional White-Bread Dressing. Choose your favorite and pair it with the ultimate companion— The Perfect Roast Turkey.

The Perfect Roast Turkey

1 (12- to 15-pound) turkey
Salt and freshly ground pepper
Stuffing
½ cup butter or margarine, melted
Garnish: spiced crabapples, fresh sage,
    thyme, and marjoram sprigs (optional)

Remove giblets and neck from turkey; reserve for other uses. Rinse turkey thoroughly inside and out with cold water; pat dry. Sprinkle body cavities of turkey with salt and pepper, and lightly pack with desired stuffing. Tuck legs under flap of skin around tail, or close cavity with skewers and truss. Tie ends of drumsticks to tail with cord. Lift wingtips up and over back and tuck under turkey.

Preheat oven to 450°. Place turkey on a rack in a roasting pan, breast side up; brush outside of bird with melted butter. Sprinkle with salt and pepper.

Insert meat thermometer into meaty part of thigh, making sure it does not touch bone.

Place turkey in preheated oven; reduce oven temperature to 325°. Bake turkey for 4½ to 5½ hours or until meat thermometer registers 185°. Baste occasionally with melted butter. If turkey begins to brown excessively, cover loosely with aluminum foil. When turkey is two-thirds done, cut cord holding drumsticks to tail to ensure that thighs are completely cooked. Turkey is done when drumsticks move up and down easily.

Let turkey stand 15 minutes before carving. Garnish, if desired. Yield: 20 to 24 servings.

Note: Cooking time is for a stuffed turkey. An unstuffed turkey requires 5 minutes less per pound.

Above: Dressed in the finest of fresh herbs, The Perfect Roast Turkey is ready for the big day. Flavorful and moist when cooked inside the bird, Yankee Stuffing is a traditional choice of the Northeast.

Yankee Stuffing

2 medium onions, coarsely chopped
4 stalks celery, coarsely chopped
1½ cups butter or margarine, melted
½ cup chopped fresh parsley
2 (24-ounce) loaves day-old white bread, cubed
¼ cup plus 2 tablespoons poultry seasoning
1½ teaspoons salt
1 teaspoon pepper
6 eggs, beaten
1 cup milk
3 (10-ounce) containers fresh Standard
  oysters (optional)

Sauté onion and celery in melted butter in a large skillet until tender. Stir in parsley and cool.

Place bread cubes in a large bowl; sprinkle with poultry seasoning, salt, and pepper, tossing to mix well. Add onion mixture; toss well. Combine eggs and milk. Drizzle over bread mixture, tossing gently. If desired, gently stir oysters into stuffing mixture.

Lightly pack about 6 cups stuffing into body cavities of turkey. Bake turkey as directed in recipe for The Perfect Roast Turkey.

Spoon remaining stuffing into a lightly greased 13" x 9" x 2" baking dish. Cover and bake at 350° for 25 minutes. Uncover and bake an additional 15 minutes or until lightly browned. Yield: 8 to 10 servings.

Chorizo-and-Corn Dressing

½ pound chorizo
1 medium onion, chopped
2 stalks celery, chopped
2 tablespoons butter or margarine, melted
1 (8¾-ounce) can cream-style corn
1 (4-ounce) can chopped green chilies,
  undrained
¼ cup chopped fresh cilantro
4 cups crumbled cornbread
8 slices white bread, toasted and cubed
¾ teaspoon salt
¼ teaspoon pepper
½ cup chicken broth

Remove and discard casing from sausage. Cook sausage in a medium skillet until browned, stirring to crumble. Drain well; set aside.

Sauté onion and celery in melted butter until tender. Stir in corn, chilies, and cilantro; set aside.

Combine cornbread and bread cubes in a large bowl; sprinkle with salt and pepper and toss well. Add sausage and onion mixture, stirring gently. Add chicken broth; stir until bread mixture is moistened.

Spoon dressing into a buttered 11" x 7" x 2" baking dish. Bake, uncovered, at 350° for 30 minutes or until lightly browned. Yield: 8 to 10 servings.

Sausage-Cornbread Dressing

½ pound bulk pork sausage
1 medium onion, chopped
4 stalks celery, chopped
2 tablespoons butter or margarine, melted
3 cups crumbled cornbread
5 slices white bread, toasted and cubed
2 teaspoons rubbed sage
¾ teaspoon salt
½ teaspoon poultry seasoning
½ teaspoon pepper
2 cups chicken broth
2 tablespoons butter or margarine, cut into
  small pieces
Garnish: fresh sage leaves and celery leaves
  (optional)

Cook sausage in a medium skillet until browned, stirring to crumble. Drain well; set aside.

Sauté onion and celery in melted butter until tender. Combine sausage, sautéed onion mixture, cornbread, and bread cubes in a large bowl; toss well. Sprinkle with sage, salt, poultry seasoning, and pepper; stir well. Add chicken broth; stir until bread mixture is moistened.

Spoon dressing into a buttered 10" x 6" x 2" baking dish and dot with butter. Bake, uncovered, at 350° for 35 minutes or until lightly browned. Garnish, if desired. Yield: 6 to 8 servings.

Traditional White-Bread Dressing

2 large onions, diced
1½ cups sliced fresh mushrooms
¾ cup butter or margarine, melted
2 (20-ounce) loaves day-old white bread
¼ cup plus 2 tablespoons milk
3 eggs, lightly beaten
1½ tablespoons rubbed sage
1 teaspoon poultry seasoning
½ teaspoon salt
¼ teaspoon pepper

Sauté onion and mushrooms in melted butter in a large skillet until tender. Set aside.

Trim crust from bread slices and reserve crust for other uses. Tear bread into bite-size pieces and place in a large bowl. Drizzle milk over bread and toss gently. Add onion mixture and eggs, tossing gently. Sprinkle with sage and remaining ingredients; stir lightly until blended.

Spoon dressing into a lightly greased 13" x 9" x 2" baking dish. Cover and bake at 350° for 30 minutes. Uncover and bake an additional 10 minutes or until lightly browned. Yield: 8 to 10 servings.

Below: Chorizo-and-Corn Dressing combines spicy pork sausage, green chilies, cream-style corn, and fresh cilantro for a Southwestern sensation.

One Cake— Four Enchanting Presentations

Imagine mastering a special cake that is sure to become your trademark. This Rich Sour Cream-Vanilla Cake will be the one. Then add impressive, yet simple, frostings to your repertoire. Cakes this spectacular will make entertaining a merry adventure.

Rich Sour Cream-Vanilla Cake

¾ cup butter or margarine, softened
½ (8-ounce) package cream cheese, softened
1½ cups sugar
3 eggs
½ cup sour cream
1¾ cups sifted cake flour
1 teaspoon vanilla extract

Cream butter and cream cheese; gradually add sugar, beating well at medium speed of an electric mixer. Add eggs, 1 at a time, beating well after each addition. Add sour cream and beat just until blended. Add flour to creamed mixture, beating just until blended. Stir in vanilla.

Pour batter into a greased and floured 9" round

Customize the Flavors

For best results, follow a cake recipe's measurements and procedures exactly. But when it comes to the cake's subtle flavors, customize them to your liking. Use any of the following flavors in place of vanilla extract: almond extract, vanilla beans, lemon extract, rum extract, butter and nut flavoring, grated lemon and orange rind, or thawed orange juice or lemonade concentrate.

cakepan with 3" sides. Bake at 325° for 1 hour or until a wooden pick inserted in center comes out clean. Cool in pan 10 minutes. Remove from pan; cool completely on a wire rack. Yield: 1 (9") cake.

Note: Cake can be made in a 9" springform pan. Cake can be frozen for up to 1 month.

Holiday Fig-and-Coconut Cake

Rich Sour Cream-Vanilla Cake
2 tablespoons butter or margarine, softened
1 cup finely chopped dried figs
¾ cup brandy
½ cup sugar
3 egg yolks
2 tablespoons butter or margarine, melted
1 cup flaked coconut
Honey-Almond Frosting (recipe follows)
¼ cup sliced almonds, toasted
7 crystallized violets

Using a pastry brush, brush loose crumbs from Rich Sour Cream-Vanilla Cake. Spread butter lightly over top and sides of cake. Set aside.

Combine figs and brandy in a small saucepan; bring to a boil. Remove from heat, cover, and let stand 30 minutes. Drain well, reserving 1 teaspoon brandy. Set aside.

Combine sugar, egg yolks, and melted butter in a small saucepan; stir well with a wire whisk. Cook over medium-low heat 5 minutes or until thickened, stirring constantly. Remove from heat and cool completely. Stir in reserved figs, brandy, and coconut. Set aside.

Spoon three-fourths of Honey-Almond Frosting into a large decorating bag fitted with a No. 4B metal tip. Pipe frosting in diagonal rows around sides of cake. Spread reserved fig mixture on top of cake. Spoon remaining frosting into a small decorating bag fitted with a No. 21 metal tip. Pipe 6 small rosettes on top of cake, 1" from edge. Pipe 1 large rosette in center of cake. Arrange almonds around rosettes to form flowers. Place a crystallized violet in the center of each flower. Yield: 1 (9") cake.
Continued on page 102.

Right: A basic buttery-rich cake is the starter for each of these stunning desserts. From top, choose the Blonde Brittle Cake, the Holiday Fig-and-Coconut Cake, or the White-Chocolate Lemon-Cream Cake.

Honey-Almond Frosting:

¾ cup butter or margarine, softened
2 cups sifted powdered sugar
1 tablespoon honey
½ teaspoon almond extract

Cream butter at medium speed of an electric mixer; gradually add sugar, beating until light and fluffy. Add honey and almond extract; beat until smooth. Yield: 1¾ cups.

White-Chocolate Lemon-Cream Cake

Rich Sour Cream-Vanilla Cake
½ cup sugar
1½ teaspoons cornstarch
¾ teaspoon grated lemon rind
¼ cup freshly squeezed lemon juice
¼ cup water
1 egg, beaten
1 cup plus 2 tablespoons whipping cream
White-Chocolate Curls (recipe follows)

Using a pastry brush, brush loose crumbs from Rich Sour Cream-Vanilla Cake. Set aside.

Combine sugar, cornstarch, and lemon rind in a heavy saucepan; stir well. Stir in juice and water. Cook over medium heat, stirring constantly, until mixture thickens and comes to a boil. Boil 1 minute, stirring constantly.

Gradually stir about half of hot mixture into beaten egg; stir into remaining hot mixture. Cook mixture over medium-low heat 2 minutes, stirring constantly, until thickened and bubbly. Remove from heat. Transfer mixture to a small bowl; cover and chill.

Beat whipping cream at high speed of an electric mixer until stiff peaks form. Stir about ½ cup whipped cream into chilled lemon mixture. Gently fold lemon mixture into remaining whipped cream. Spread over top and sides of cake. Garnish with White-Chocolate Curls. Cover and chill before serving. Yield: 1 (9") cake.

Below: Start with the Rich Sour Cream-Vanilla Cake; then pour on a glossy chocolate ganache to create this elegant Mocha-Pecan Torte.

White-Chocolate Curls:

4 (4-ounce) bars premier white chocolate

Place 1 bar of chocolate on waxed paper in microwave. Microwave, uncovered, at HIGH 30 to 35 seconds or until chocolate feels slightly tacky, not firm. (If chocolate is too hard, curls will break; if too soft, chocolate will not curl.)

For each curl, gently pull a vegetable peeler across length of chocolate until curl forms; transfer to a paper plate. Chill curls until ready to use. Repeat procedure with remaining chocolate bars. Yield: 1 pound White Chocolate Curls.

Note: Chocolate bar may break. Chocolate curls can still be formed using chocolate pieces.

Blonde Brittle Cake

Rich Sour Cream-Vanilla Cake
5 ounces commercial peanut brittle, divided
¼ cup plus 2 tablespoons sugar
¼ cup maple syrup
3 egg yolks
1 cup butter or margarine, softened
¾ cup sifted powdered sugar
½ teaspoon maple flavoring

Using a pastry brush, brush loose crumbs from Rich Sour Cream-Vanilla Cake. Set aside.

Chop 3 ounces peanut brittle; set aside. Position knife blade in food processor bowl; add remaining peanut brittle, and process until finely crushed. Set aside.

Combine sugar and syrup in a small saucepan; bring to a boil over medium heat, stirring occasionally. Boil 1 minute and remove from heat. Beat egg yolks at high speed of an electric mixer until thick and lemon colored (about 5 minutes). Gradually stir about one-fourth of hot mixture into beaten egg yolks; stir into remaining hot mixture. Cook over medium-low heat 3 to 4 minutes, stirring constantly.

Remove egg yolk mixture from heat and transfer to a large mixing bowl. Beat at medium speed of an electric mixer 5 minutes or until mixture is completely cool. Add softened butter, 1 tablespoon at a time, beating well after each addition. Add powdered sugar and flavoring; beat until smooth.

Spread frosting on top and sides of cake. Pat finely crushed peanut brittle onto sides of cake. Evenly space 5 (1") strips of waxed paper on top of cake, parallel to each other. Pat chopped peanut brittle between strips. Carefully peel off waxed paper, leaving a striped design. Yield: 1 (9") cake.

Mocha-Pecan Torte

2 ounces semisweet chocolate morsels
2 teaspoons shortening, divided
8 pecan halves
Rich Sour Cream-Vanilla Cake
2 tablespoons plus 2 teaspoons Kahlúa or other coffee-flavored liqueur, divided
¼ cup apple jelly
½ cup plus 3 tablespoons whipping cream
2 tablespoons light corn syrup
6 ounces Swiss dark chocolate, finely chopped
½ teaspoon vanilla extract
3 ounces milk chocolate morsels

Combine semisweet chocolate morsels and 1 teaspoon shortening in a small saucepan. Cook over low heat until chocolate and shortening melt, stirring frequently. Remove from heat. Dip 1 end of each pecan half into chocolate; allow excess to drain back into saucepan. Place on cookie sheet lined with waxed paper. Chill.

Using a pastry brush, brush loose crumbs from Rich Sour Cream-Vanilla Cake. Drizzle 2 tablespoons Kahlúa over top of cake.

Melt apple jelly in a small saucepan over low heat. Cool slightly. Brush jelly over top and sides of cake. Chill.

Combine whipping cream and syrup in a medium saucepan; bring to a boil over medium heat. Remove from heat and stir in dark chocolate. Let stand 1 minute. Gently stir until chocolate melts. Stir in vanilla and remaining teaspoons Kahlúa.

Place cake on a wire rack over waxed paper. Pour dark chocolate mixture completely over cake, letting excess drip onto waxed paper. Chill at least 10 minutes. Transfer cake to a serving platter.

Combine milk chocolate morsels and remaining 1 teaspoon shortening in a small saucepan. Cook over low heat until chocolate and shortening melt, stirring frequently. Remove from heat and cool slightly. Spoon melted chocolate mixture into a zip-top plastic bag; remove air and seal plastic bag. (A decorating bag fitted with a No. 2 round tip can also be used.) Snip a tiny hole in 1 corner of zip-top bag and pipe chocolate mixture in a decorative design over cake. Place chocolate-dipped pecan halves around edge of cake. Yield: 1 (9") cake.

Ideas

Quick Canapés

Hostesses often shy away from canapés. The bite-size appetizers have a reputation of being delicious to eat but time-consuming to create. Thanks to these simple recipes, however, canapés are making a comeback.

The Best Bases

Tiny, crisp pastry shells ready for a variety of fillings can be purchased in the gourmet section of the grocery store, along with specialty crackers and breadsticks. The shells require no preparation. Just stuff them with an appetizer filling of your choice and serve.

While not classically considered canapé bases, fresh produce—mushrooms, cherry tomatoes, zucchini, and Belgian endive—provides a healthful alternative to traditional bases.

Choose a Filling

Choose one of the savory fillings below for delicious *hors d'oeuvres* in a snap. To add a finishing touch, embellish the stuffed canapés with small sprigs of dill or parsley.

Right: Keep ready-made appetizer pastry shells on hand for when last-minute guests drop by. Mushrooms, cucumbers, cherry tomatoes, bell peppers, and endive also make easy shells.

Below: Colorful Italian Zucchini Filling, in foreground, pairs well with either zucchini shells or commercial pastry shells. Cucumber-Salmon Filling offers a creamy contrast to crunchy Belgian endive.

Left: Garnish Chicken-Apple-Salad Filling with a twist of red apple peel.

Chicken-Apple-Salad Filling

2 (5-ounce) cans white chicken in spring
    water, drained and flaked
½ cup finely chopped apple
¼ cup plus 2 tablespoons sour cream
¼ cup mayonnaise
¾ to 1 teaspoon curry powder
½ teaspoon salt
¼ teaspoon pepper

Combine all ingredients, stirring well. Cover and chill at least 1 hour. Yield: 2 cups.

Sweet-Onion Filling

2 (3-ounce) packages cream cheese, softened
⅔ cup commercial sweet-onion relish, drained
½ cup canned whole kernel corn, drained
1 (2-ounce) jar diced pimiento, drained
2 tablespoons mayonnaise
⅛ teaspoon pepper
Dash of garlic salt

Beat cream cheese at medium speed of an electric mixer until smooth; stir in relish and remaining ingredients. Cover and chill at least 1 hour. Yield: 1⅔ cups.

Crab-and-Bacon Filling

¾ pound fresh crabmeat, drained and flaked
6 slices bacon, cooked and crumbled
½ cup sour cream
½ cup mayonnaise
¼ cup chopped water chestnuts
2 tablespoons sherry
⅛ teaspoon garlic powder

Combine all ingredients, stirring well. Cover and chill at least 1 hour. Yield: 2⅔ cups.

Italian Zucchini Filling

1½ cups finely diced zucchini
¼ cup chopped fresh mushrooms
¼ cup chopped sweet red pepper
1 tablespoon grated onion
2 teaspoons olive oil
¼ cup seeded, chopped tomato
2 tablespoons freshly grated Parmesan cheese
¾ teaspoon dried Italian seasoning

Sauté first 4 ingredients in olive oil until tender. Stir in tomato, cheese, and seasoning. Yield: 1½ cups.

Cucumber-Salmon Filling

1 (7½-ounce) can red salmon, drained
1 (8-ounce) package cream cheese, softened
1 tablespoon Chablis or other dry white wine
½ cup chopped, seeded cucumber
½ teaspoon dried whole dillweed
¼ teaspoon salt
¼ teaspoon pepper
Dash of ground red pepper

Remove skin and bones from salmon, if desired; flake salmon with a fork. Set aside.
Beat cream cheese and wine at medium speed of an electric mixer until smooth; stir in salmon, cucumber, and remaining ingredients. Cover and chill at least 1 hour. Yield: 1¾ cups.

Below: Bright yellow pepper, sliced cucumber, flaky pastry, and zesty fillings are easily combined for these party-perfect hors d'oeuvres.

Pleasures of the Season

Ribbons and Bows

Something about the holidays awakens in each of us the little girl who adores dressing up for parties. To make these fashionable accessories for partygoers of all ages, use a few simple techniques to transform plain ribbon into festive finery.

For all the projects pictured, you will find instructions under the ribbon technique used to make each item. And because the ribbon techniques are so versatile, you can easily create bright, beribboned trims of your own design.

Fused Ribbons

To fuse 1 ribbon to each edge of a wider ribbon (see yellow-and-blue bow, on opposite page): Determine length you want finished ribbon to be. Cut to this measurement 1 length of wide ribbon, 2 lengths of narrow ribbon, and 2 strips of paper-backed fusible web. (Web should be about half as wide as narrow ribbon.) Following manufacturer's instructions, fuse 1 web strip just inside each long edge of wrong side of wide ribbon. Peel paper backing from web strips. Place 1 narrow ribbon on each web strip, aligning inside edge of ribbon with inside edge of web, and fuse in place.

To fuse a narrow ribbon along center of a wider ribbon (see green-and-blue bow, on opposite page): Cut a strip of paper-backed fusible web that is about ½" narrower than narrow ribbon and use technique described above, except center and fuse narrow ribbon on right side of wide ribbon.

To make hair bow: Thread fused ribbon through a purchased belt buckle, centering buckle on ribbon length. Fold ends of ribbon to back and thread through buckle again to secure. If desired, make streamers for bow by centering 1 narrow ribbon along center of 1 wide ribbon; hand-stitch ends together at 1 end, pulling thread to gather slightly. Secure thread. Tack gathered end of streamers to back of bow. Trim ends of streamers as desired. Hot-glue bow to French-clasp barrette hardware.

Ruched Ribbon

To make ruched ribbon (see gold-metallic-trimmed barrette, on opposite page): Determine length you want finished section to be and multiply by 3; cut to this measurement 1 length of wire-edged ribbon (also called French ribbon). Referring to Diagram 1, turn under raw ends and run a gathering stitch in zigzag pattern along entire length of ribbon. Referring to Diagram 2, pull thread to gather. Secure thread.

To make barrette: Hot-glue ruched ribbon to top of French-clasp barrette hardware. To make gold trim, tack gold beads to a length of gold metallic trim at regular intervals; turn raw ends of trim under and hot-glue along center of ruched ribbon.

To make rosette hair bow (below): Cut about 3 yards of wire-edged ribbon. Gather ribbon as described above. Coil ruched ribbon to form a 3-tier rosette, tacking edges of ribbon on wrong side to secure. Tack rosette to center of red bow made from wide grosgrain ribbon. If desired, glue a tiny red Christmas ball to center of rosette.

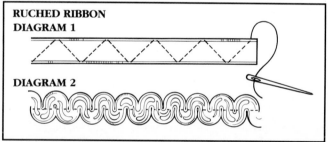

RUCHED RIBBON
DIAGRAM 1

DIAGRAM 2

Left: Create these hair bows by using paper-backed fusible web to bind together two kinds of richly textured ribbons (see Fused Ribbons, above). To make the gold-metallic-trimmed barrette, use the gathering technique called ruching (see Ruched Ribbon, above right). Instructions for making the Pleated-Ribbon Star are on page 110. For instructions on making the Perforated-Paper Star shown on top of the pleated star, see page 45.

Right: A special bow or headband accents a favorite party dress. The satin ribbon headband is made by pleating double-sided ribbon for a stunning effect (see Box-Pleated Ribbon, page 110). The red bow is made by coiling ruched ribbon into an elegant rosette (see Ruched Ribbon, above right).

Ribbon Fringe

For base, determine length you want each finished fringe to be and cut a length of grosgrain ribbon to this measurement. For fringe, cut an assortment of ribbons varying in colors, textures, widths, and lengths. Tie ribbons in knots and bows around base ribbon. Knot ends of narrow ribbons. Trim ends of wide ribbons as desired. If desired, knot or tack tiny jingle bells or Christmas balls to ends of desired number of ribbons.

To make epaulets (below): Use safety pins to attach base of 1 ribbon fringe to each shoulder of a shirt, sweater, or sweatshirt.

Gathered-Ribbon Flowers

To make 1 ribbon flower: Run a gathering stitch along center of a length of ribbon. Pull thread to gather, arranging ribbon to form a circle of desired size. If gathered circle is too full, cut excess ribbon. Turn raw ends under and stitch ends together. Tack ribbon together in center to make flower.

To make button covers (below): For each cover, hot-glue scrap of gold metallic trim around edge on back of 1 faux jewel. Hot-glue back of jewel to center of ribbon flower. Hot-glue flower to purchased button-cover form.

Following manufacturer's instructions, attach button covers to buttons on shirt.

Below: Transform ordinary garments into party-ready attire with epaulets made of Ribbon Fringe and fancy button covers made of Gathered-Ribbon Flowers (for both, see above).

Box-Pleated Ribbon

Determine length you want finished ribbon to be and multiply by 3½. Cut to this measurement 1 length of satin ribbon with contrasting colors on either side. Referring to Diagram 1, fold ⅝" box pleats in ribbon, hand-basting pleats along center with matching thread as indicated to secure. Referring to Diagram 2 and working on 1 side of ribbon only, pinch top and bottom edges of each box pleat together and tack at center. Using matching thread, tack a small faux pearl or bead to center of each pinched pleat, wrapping thread once around pinched pleat to compress it.

To make headband (page 109): Tack pleated ribbon to purchased cloth-covered headband, turning raw ends of ribbon under at ends of headband.

BOX-PLEATED RIBBON

⅝"

DIAGRAM 1

DIAGRAM 2

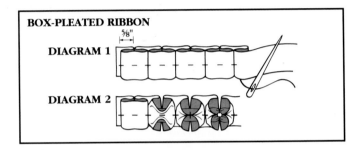

Pleated-Ribbon Stars

Materials for 1 star:
1 (9½") length of 2"-wide stiff plaid
  ribbon
thread to match ribbon
glue
faux jewel (optional)
Perforated-Paper Star (see page 45)
  (optional)

Fold ribbon accordion-style in 10 (½") or 12 (⅜") pleats, creasing pleats sharply. With matching thread, tack pleats together at 1 end; secure thread. Do not unfold pleats. Holding tacked end in 1 hand, make a ½" diagonal cut on opposite end, cutting through all layers. Opening up pleats, match raw ends of ribbon to form star; glue ends together to secure. If desired, glue faux jewel or Perforated-Paper Star to center of pleated star.

Santa-and-Me Photo Album

What is a child's favorite thing about Christmas? Any youngster might say that the annual visit with Santa is one of the season's best events. This ritual deserves a special album for displaying those cherished photographs.

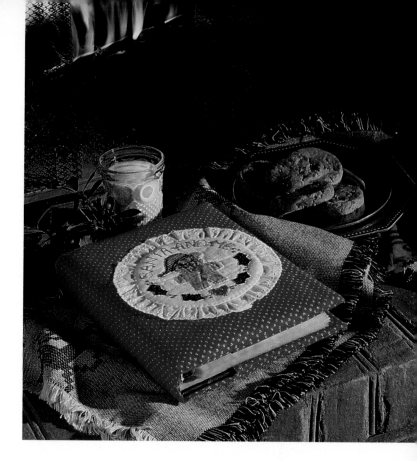

Materials:
patterns on page 153
tracing paper
water-soluble marker
7" square of white cotton
scraps of print fabric for appliqué pieces: tan, light green, dark green, red
embroidery floss: green, brown, red
thread to match fabrics
⅓ yard of thin batting
white quilting thread
¾ yard (1"-wide) pregathered white eyelet lace
1 large photo album or 3-ring binder, with cover at least 9" square
½ yard (45"-wide) red print fabric
fabric glue

Note: Circle pattern includes ¼" seam allowance. Instructions are given for machine-appliqué. If you wish to appliqué by hand, add ⅛" seam allowance to pattern pieces and turn under seam allowance before appliquéing.

Using tracing paper and water-soluble marker, transfer circle pattern to white fabric. Lightly mark placement for words and appliqué shapes inside marked circle. Using tracing paper and marker, transfer appliqué patterns to fabric scraps. Do not cut out.

Use 2 strands of floss for embroidery. Using green floss, straightstitch nose and mouth. Using brown floss, satin-stitch eyes and straightstitch eyelashes. Using red floss, satin-stitch cheeks; straightstitch bow tie; and work 2-wrap French knots for buttons.

Cut out appliqué pieces. Using narrow zigzag stitch, machine-appliqué pieces on white circle. Also stitch seam details on bear (see pattern).

Using red floss, straightstitch all words and work 3-wrap French knots for dots between the words.

Satin-stitch berries and pom-pom at tip of hat.

Cut out appliquéd circle. From batting, cut a 6" circle. Center batting circle on wrong side of appliquéd circle and baste. Using quilting thread, outline-quilt ⅛" from edge around bear, leaves, and heart. Remove basting. Turn raw edge of circle under ¼" and press. Beginning at bottom center of circle, slipstitch lace around edge of wrong side of circle. Where lace meets at bottom, turn end of lace under and continue stitching to secure end.

To make pattern of album cover, open album or binder on top of tracing paper so that panels and spine lie flat. Trace outline of album and cut out.

Using marker, transfer cover pattern twice to red print fabric and once to batting, adding ¼" seam allowance to all sides. Cut 2 from red fabric for cover and lining and 1 from batting.

For album sleeves, from red print fabric, cut 2 rectangles, 6" wide and as tall as cover pieces. Turn 1 long edge of each rectangle under ¼" and stitch.

With right sides up and raw edges aligned, baste 1 sleeve piece to each end of lining piece. With raw edges aligned, stack batting; lining/sleeves, right side up; and album cover, right side down. Stitch through all layers, leaving an opening for turning. Trim seams and excess batting and clip corners. Turn between sleeves and album cover. Slipstitch opening closed. Insert album into cover. Center appliquéd circle on front and glue in place. Let dry.

Above: This welcoming chapel nestled beside a pair of quaint winter cottages makes a lovely holiday centerpiece. Designed for The Continental Bakery in Birmingham, Alabama, by James McDaniel, these shortbread structures will last the entire Christmas season if nibblers can be dissuaded.

A Snow-Frosted Village

For a sweet departure from traditional dark-spiced gingerbread, try your hand at building a snow-dusted Shortbread Cottage or Chapel.

Shortbread Cottage

patterns on page 150
1 cup butter
1 cup sugar
1 egg
4 cups all-purpose flour
1 teaspoon baking powder
¼ teaspoon salt
¼ teaspoon vanilla extract
Quick Buttercream Frosting (recipe follows)

Transfer patterns to paper and cut out. Set aside.
Cream butter at medium speed of an electric mixer; gradually add sugar, beating until light and fluffy. Add egg, beating well. Combine flour, baking powder, and salt. Add to creamed mixture, beating well. Beat in vanilla. (Dough will be stiff.)

Pat dough into a 10" square on a lightly floured surface. Wrap in plastic wrap and chill 1 hour.
Divide dough into fourths. Using 1 portion of dough at a time as needed, place dough on a sheet of waxed paper or parchment paper. Cover dough with a large sheet of plastic wrap and roll dough to ⅛" thickness. Remove plastic wrap and place patterns on dough. Using a sharp knife, cut out front and back, cutting to but not through waxed paper. Repeat for sides. Using a 1"-diameter round cookie cutter, cut out windows on side walls. Carefully lift waxed paper and dough shapes to a cookie sheet. Bake on waxed paper at 350° for 8 to 10 minutes. Cool slightly on cookie sheet. Transfer to a wire rack and cool completely.
Repeat with remaining dough for chimney pieces and 2 (6½" x 3¾") rectangles for roof. Reserve excess dough for other uses.

Quick Buttercream Frosting:

¼ cup butter, softened
1 (16-ounce) box powdered sugar, sifted
dash of salt
½ teaspoon vanilla extract
3 to 4 tablespoons milk
red, green liquid or paste food coloring

Beat butter at medium speed of an electric mixer for 1 minute. Gradually add powdered sugar and salt until blended. Add vanilla and beat well. Add milk, 1 tablespoon at a time, beating until mixture is light and fluffy but still holds its shape. Tint frosting with coloring in quantities described below. Keep frosting covered until ready to use. Yield: About 3 cups.

To Assemble Cottage:

Prepare base for cottage by covering an 8" x 10" piece of heavy cardboard with gold or aluminum foil.

Half-fill a pastry bag fitted with No. 29 tip with frosting. Pipe a thick line of piping on 1 inside edge of side wall. Place 1 edge of front wall against frosted inside edge of side wall. Let frosting set, about 1 minute. Pipe frosting along bottom edge of both pieces. Position walls on base and let set. Repeat for remaining side and back walls.

Pipe frosting along top long edge of front wall and up 1 side of each sloping edge of side walls. Position 1 roof piece against frosted edges of walls and hold until set, about 1 minute. Pipe frosting along edges where 2 roof pieces will meet. Repeat on other side of roof. Pipe additional frosting to fill any spaces along this or any other seam.

Pipe frosting along 1 long edge and top of door and attach to cottage front in open position. Let set.

To attach chimney, pipe frosting on slanted edge of 1 chimney side. Position piped edge on front of roof just left of center. Let frosting set. Pipe frosting on bottom and 2 sides of chimney back. Attach to short edge of chimney side. Pipe frosting on slanted edge of remaining chimney side. Position on roof, joining with frosted edge of chimney back. Pipe frosting on inside long edges of chimney front and join with chimney sides. Let frosting set.

Tint about ½ cup frosting green and ½ cup red. Spoon green frosting into pastry bag fitted with No. 29 tip and pipe wreath around round windows and greenery over door and in square window sill. Spoon red frosting into pastry bag fitted with No. 47

tip and pipe frosting on chimney. Let frosting set.

Change tip on red pastry bag to No. 4 tip and pipe berries and bow on wreath and berries on greenery.

Using white frosting and No. 4 tip, pipe mortar for bricks on chimney. Let frosting set.

Change tip on white frosting pastry bag to No. 29 tip and pipe a decorative border along base and all seams of cottage and chimney. Add puffs of snow on roof and dust with powdered sugar.

Let cottage sit for at least 36 hours before moving.

Shortbread Chapel

patterns and roof design on pages 151-52
2 batches of Shortbread (recipe precedes)
Quick Buttercream Frosting (recipe precedes)

Follow instructions for Shortbread Cottage above, substituting chapel patterns. Cut out decorative details with cookie cutters or sharp knife. Also cut and bake 2 (9½" x 4¼") rectangles for roof pieces.

Prepare base for chapel by covering a 9" x 12" piece of heavy cardboard with gold or aluminum foil.

Half-fill a pastry bag fitted with No. 29 tip with frosting. Referring to cottage assembly instructions, join walls of chapel. Pipe frosting along curved edge of both doors and attach to chapel front in open position. Let frosting set about 1 minute.

To attach steeple, pipe frosting on short slanted edges of steeple front. Position piped edge on front of roof just left of center. Let frosting set. Pipe frosting on bottom and 1 long edge of steeple side. Attach to 1 long edge of steeple front. Pipe frosting on short edges and 1 long edge of steeple back. Position on roof, joining with steeple side. Pipe frosting along 2 long edges of steeple side and attach to steeple front and back. Let frosting set.

Using green frosting and No. 29 tip, pipe greenery over doors and in window sills as shown in photograph. Change to No. 4 tip and, referring to roof design, pipe decorative detail on roof and steeple.

Using red frosting and No. 4 tip, pipe berries onto greenery. Let frosting set.

Prepare a second batch of frosting if necessary. Using white frosting and No. 29 tip, pipe decorative border along base and all seams of chapel and steeple. Dust with powdered sugar.

Let chapel sit for at least 36 hours before moving.

Above: In Scandinavian countries, Saint Lucia's Day marks the beginning of Christmas celebrations with colorful street festivals. This little cherub is part of the school-age Santa Lucia singers, who parade down Sixth Street singing the song "Santa Lucia" in Swedish.

Small Town Celebration

Heading west on Highway 70 from Denver—don't blink! You might miss the quiet little town of Georgetown, Colorado. Unless, that is, you happen to be in the area on one of the first two weekends of December. Then, mysterious sounds of bagpipes in the cool mountain air might lure you off the highway to explore this old silver-mining town.

Georgetown (population: 800) is tiny, but its annual Christmas celebration is anything but small. For the past 32 years its residents have heralded the season with their Georgetown Christmas Market, an outdoor festival of old-world European traditions presented with a down-home flair.

The entire community takes part in the festival. The townspeople work hard to decorate their storefronts and homes with holiday finery in preparation for the event. Throughout the year they search for performing groups to represent different ethnic backgrounds—Swedish, Norwegian, Danish, English, and Scottish, to name a few.

The Christmas Market features this rich mélange of traditions because they are important to Georgetown's own history. In the late 19th century, during the heyday of the town's silver-mining industry, groups of Europeans settled in Georgetown in hopes of making their fortune. Today, many of the town's residents claim direct European lineage.

Right: The Isle of Mull/Saint Andrew Pipe and Drums group proudly perform Scottish melodies with their Great Highland bagpipes. The group, whose kilts and bagpipes are handmade in Scotland, strive to preserve Scottish culture.

This heritage is proudly flaunted during the Christmas Market. People travel from all over the state to revel in the spirited music and gather a taste of a European-style celebration—Scottish bagpipers in red plaid kilts, children chanting songs in celebration of Saint Lucia, and groups of Scandinavian and European folk dancers and musicians.

The musicians and dancers lead the procession down Sixth Street to Strousse Park, the focal point of the Market. Amid booths of handmade crafts and ethnic cuisine, people congregate to join in the merrymaking with their own Christmas carols. An old mining cart has been converted into a pit for roasting chestnuts. Mouth-watering scents of Swedish pastries, such as *lussekattre* (Saint Lucia cake), swirl through the air; and a local Catholic church serves German bratwurst on rye rolls, a treat that has become a favorite of the townspeople.

It is an honor to be invited to sell one's handmade creations at the Christmas Market. There are wooden chests, toys, and ornaments painted with the Norwegian technique of "rosemaling"—colorful flowers and swirls. For many years one woman has traveled from Denmark to sell her knitted sweaters and hats at the market. Local craftspeople show their work as well—a woman from Georgetown who raises angora rabbits sells luxurious knitted accessories made from hand-dyed-and-spun rabbit fur.

Folks in Georgetown are proud of their small community, as is seen by their determination to preserve its heritage. The Georgetown Christmas Market, now one of the oldest outdoor Christmas markets in the United States, is a tribute to their dedication.

Above: In keeping with the European focus of the Georgetown Christmas Market, this shop window boasts a collection of fine hand-blown glass ornaments from Germany. Janice Moore, owner of this shop, and Pattie Fraley are co-chairs of the annual celebration. For information on the Georgetown Christmas Market, see the source listing on page 154.

Below: The cowboy driving this wagon, Buff Rutherford, is a third-generation Georgetownian; his grandparents were part of the first Swedish immigration to the area. With his wife, Mary Lou, and their Belgian horses, Rusty and Rowdy, Buff delights children and adults alike with song-filled hayrides through historical Georgetown.

Tidings of Sweet Joy

What giddy delight luscious desserts offer! Here's a choice of seven showstoppers for the Christmas season—from creamy puddings to spiked nog. Choose three or four for an impressive "desserts only" get-together or choose just one for a late-night treat by the fire.

Cranberry-Apple Kuchen

1½ cups all-purpose flour
⅓ cup sugar
¾ teaspoon baking powder
7 tablespoons butter or margarine, softened
1 egg, beaten
2 teaspoons water
½ teaspoon vanilla extract
¼ teaspoon almond extract
½ cup chopped macadamia nuts
½ cup sugar
3 tablespoons all-purpose flour
½ teaspoon grated orange rind
1 egg
1 tablespoon butter or margarine
Orange-Cranberry Filling (recipe follows)
2 medium cooking apples, peeled, cored, and
   quartered
Powdered sugar

Combine 1½ cups flour, ⅓ cup sugar, and baking powder in a large bowl; cut in 7 tablespoons butter with a pastry blender until mixture resembles coarse meal. Combine beaten egg, water, and extracts. Sprinkle over dry ingredients and stir with a fork just until moistened. Shape dough into a ball. Press dough on bottom and 1½" up sides of a 9" springform pan. Chill at least 15 minutes.

Position knife blade in food processor bowl; add macadamia nuts and next 3 ingredients. Process 10 seconds or until nuts are ground. Add egg and 1 tablespoon butter; process just until blended. Spread mixture over chilled dough crust. Spread Orange-Cranberry Filling over nut mixture, leaving a 1" margin around edge of pan.

Left: Guests may have a difficult time choosing between these tempting selections, so why not suggest a taste of each? From top: fruity Cranberry-Apple Kuchen, demitasses of cool and creamy Kahlúa-Drenched Pudding, and a chocolate-filigree-trimmed Vanilla-Mint Cheesecake.

Place apple quarters, cored side down, on a cutting surface. Cut thin lengthwise slits in each quarter, cutting to, but not through, cored side. Arrange apple quarters, side by side, around outside edge of dough crust. Bake at 350° for 1 hour or until crust is lightly browned. Cool 10 minutes in pan on a wire rack. Carefully remove sides of pan and cool completely on a wire rack. Dust with powdered sugar before serving. Yield: 10 to 12 servings.

Orange-Cranberry Filling:

2 cups fresh cranberries
⅔ cup orange juice
½ cup sugar

Combine cranberries, orange juice, and sugar in medium saucepan; bring to a boil over medium heat, stirring constantly. Cook 3 minutes or until cranberry skins pop. Reduce heat and simmer 25 to 30 minutes or until thick, stirring constantly. Remove from heat and cool. Yield: About 1½ cups.

Note: Kuchen may be refrigerated in a tightly covered container up to 3 days.

Vanilla-Mint Cheesecake

2 cups chocolate wafer crumbs
¼ cup plus 2 tablespoons butter or
   margarine, melted
3 (4.67-ounce) packages chocolate-covered
   mint wafer candies, divided
3 (8-ounce) packages cream cheese, softened
¾ cup sugar
3 eggs
1 (8-ounce) carton sour cream
1 vanilla bean
2 (1-ounce) semisweet chocolate squares,
   melted

To prepare crust, combine crumbs and butter in a medium bowl; stir well. Press mixture firmly on bottom and 1¾" up sides of a 9" springform pan. Bake at 350° for 10 minutes. Set aside to cool.

Position knife blade in food processor bowl; add 2 packages of mint wafer candies. Process 15 seconds or until finely chopped. Set aside.

For cheesecake filling, beat cream cheese at medium speed of an electric mixer until smooth.

Continued on next page.

Gradually add sugar, beating well. Add eggs, 1 at a time, beating just until blended after each addition. Stir in sour cream.

Split vanilla bean in half lengthwise; scrape vanilla seeds from bean. Stir vanilla seeds and chopped mint wafer candies into cheesecake mixture.

Pour mixture into prepared crust. Bake at 350° for 45 minutes or until cheesecake is almost set. Turn oven off and partially open oven door; leave cheesecake in oven 1 hour. Remove cheesecake from oven and cool to room temperature on a wire rack. Chill thoroughly.

For garnish, spoon melted chocolate into a zip-top plastic bag; remove air and seal plastic bag. (A decorating bag with a No. 2 or 3 round tip can also be used.) Snip a small hole in 1 corner of zip-top bag and drizzle Christmas tree designs on a baking sheet lined with waxed paper; freeze until firm.

Pull a vegetable peeler down sides of remaining mint wafer candies to make tiny shavings. (Candies may break, but can still be shaved.)

To serve, carefully remove sides of springform pan. Gently remove Christmas trees from waxed paper. Garnish cheesecake with mint wafer candy shavings and chocolate trees. Yield: 10 to 12 servings.

Kahlúa-Drenched Pudding

½ (10¾-ounce) frozen pound cake, thawed
2 (3-ounce) packages cream cheese, softened
1¼ cups whipping cream
½ cup plus 2 tablespoons sifted powdered
  sugar, divided
2½ tablespoons Kahlúa or other coffee-
  flavored liqueur, divided
¾ teaspoon vanilla extract
¼ cup strong brewed coffee or espresso
Grated chocolate shavings
Garnish: commercial mocha-flavored
  chocolate sticks

Cut pound cake crosswise into 12 slices. Using a 1½" cookie cutter, cut each slice into 2 circles, avoiding crust. Set circles aside.

Beat cream cheese at high speed of an electric mixer until light and fluffy. Gradually add cream and ½ cup powdered sugar, beating until smooth. Stir in 1½ tablespoons Kahlúa and vanilla. Set aside.

Combine remaining powdered sugar, Kahlúa, and coffee; stir until sugar dissolves.

Spoon 1 tablespoon cream cheese mixture into

each of 8 (⅓-cup) demitasse cups. Place 1 cake circle on top of each cream cheese mixture; brush with coffee mixture. Repeat layering procedure twice. Top each serving with remaining cream cheese mixture and chocolate shavings. Chill several hours. Let stand at room temperature 30 minutes before serving. Garnish with chocolate sticks, if desired. Yield: 8 servings.

Grand Marnier Mousse in Puff-Pastry Ring

Parchment paper
1⅓ cups water
⅔ cup butter
1⅓ cups all-purpose flour
¼ teaspoon salt
6 eggs
1¾ cups sugar
½ cup plus 2 tablespoons cornstarch
1 tablespoon grated orange rind
⅛ teaspoon salt
3 cups plus 2 tablespoons orange juice
5 egg yolks
1½ tablespoons Grand Marnier or other
  orange-flavored liqueur
1 cup plus 2 tablespoons whipping cream,
  divided
Garnish: kumquats

Mark and cut out a 9" circle from parchment paper. Turn over and place on a greased baking sheet; set aside.

Combine water and butter in a medium saucepan; bring to a boil. Combine flour and ¼ teaspoon salt; stir well. Add to butter mixture, all at once, stirring vigorously over medium-high heat until mixture leaves sides of pan and forms a smooth ball. Remove from heat and cool 2 minutes.

Add eggs 1 at a time, beating thoroughly with a wooden spoon after each addition until dough is smooth. Spoon dough into a pastry bag fitted with a large fluted tip. Working quickly, pipe dough onto prepared baking sheet, just inside edges of parchment-paper circle, to form 10 rosettes joined in a wreath shape. Bake at 400° for 48 minutes or until puffed and golden. Cool on a wire rack away from drafts.

To prepare mousse, combine sugar, cornstarch, orange rind, and ⅛ teaspoon salt in a saucepan.

Gradually add orange juice. Cook over medium heat, stirring constantly, until thick and bubbly.

Beat egg yolks until thick and lemon colored. Gradually add one-fourth of hot orange juice mixture to yolks; then add to remaining hot mixture, stirring constantly. Cook over medium-low heat, stirring constantly, for 8 minutes. Remove from heat. Stir in Grand Marnier. Transfer to a large bowl. Cover and chill thoroughly.

Beat whipping cream at high speed of an electric mixer until stiff peaks form. Stir ½ cup whipped cream into cooled orange mixture. Gently fold remaining whipped cream into orange mixture. Set aside.

Cut top third off puff pastry ring horizontally. This will separate pastry top into several 2- or 3-puff segments. Discard soft dough inside. Spoon mousse into pastry ring. Replace segments of pastry top. Garnish with kumquats, if desired. Yield: 10 servings.

Note: Serve immediately.

Spiced Pumpkin Bismarcks

2 packages dry yeast
½ cup plus 1 teaspoon sugar, divided
½ cup warm water (105° to 115°)
½ cup cooked, mashed pumpkin
2 eggs, lightly beaten
3 tablespoons butter or margarine, melted
1 teaspoon ground cinnamon
1 teaspoon salt
4 cups all-purpose flour, divided
¾ cup strawberry, raspberry, or currant jelly
1 egg white, lightly beaten
Vegetable oil
½ teaspoon ground cinnamon

Dissolve yeast and 1 teaspoon sugar in warm water in a large bowl; let stand 5 minutes. Add pumpkin and next 4 ingredients; beat at medium speed of
Continued on next page.

Below: This edible wreath combines puff pastry with a light citrus mousse laced with Grand Marnier. The puff pastry is piped directly onto a baking sheet, making this a much simpler recipe than it may appear.

119

an electric mixer until well blended. Add 2 cups flour; beat 2 minutes at medium speed. Stir in enough of remaining flour to make a soft dough.

Turn dough out onto a well-floured surface and knead until smooth and elastic (about 5 minutes). Place in a greased bowl, turning to grease top. Cover and let rise in a warm place (85°), free from drafts, 45 minutes or until doubled in bulk.

Punch dough down and divide in half. Cover half of dough and set aside. Roll remaining half to ¼" thickness and cut into 18 (3") circles.

Place 9 dough circles on a greased and floured baking sheet. Place 2 teaspoons jelly in center of each circle. Brush edge of each jelly-topped circle with egg white. Place 1 of 9 remaining dough circles over each jelly-filled circle; pinch edges to seal.

Repeat procedure with remaining half of dough and jelly. Cover and let rise in a warm place, free from drafts, 45 minutes or until doubled in bulk.

Pour oil to a depth of 2" to 3" in a Dutch oven; heat to 375°. Fry 2 to 3 bismarcks at a time 1 minute on each side or until golden brown. Drain well on paper towels.

Combine remaining ½ cup sugar and ½ teaspoon ground cinnamon in a paper bag. Add bismarcks, 1 at a time, and fold end of bag to seal. Shake bag gently to coat bismarcks. Serve warm or at room temperature. Yield: 1½ dozen.

Brandied Apricot Nog

8 ounces dried apricots
1 cup water
½ cup sugar
1 (3") cinnamon stick
2 quarts milk, divided
2 cups half-and-half
1 tablespoon vanilla extract
½ teaspoon ground nutmeg
¾ cup brandy

Combine first 4 ingredients in a medium saucepan. Bring to a boil; cover, reduce heat, and simmer 20 minutes or until apricots are tender. Remove from heat and cool. Remove and discard cinnamon stick.

Combine apricot mixture and 3 cups milk in container of an electric blender. Cover mixture and process 1 minute or until smooth. Combine apricot mixture, remaining 5 cups milk, half-and-half, vanilla, and nutmeg in a large bowl and stir well. Cover

mixture and chill at least 8 hours.

To serve, pour milk mixture into a punch bowl. Add brandy, stirring gently. Yield: 13 cups.

Chocolate Irish-Cream Punch

2 quarts chocolate ice cream, divided
4 cups ice cubes, divided
1 cup Irish Cream liqueur, chilled and divided
½ cup light rum, chilled and divided
Whipped cream
Garnish: chocolate shavings

Combine 2 cups ice cream, 1 cup ice cubes, ¼ cup Irish Cream, and 2 tablespoons rum in container of electric blender; cover and process until smooth. Pour mixture into a punch bowl. Repeat procedure 3 times. Top with whipped cream and garnish, if desired. Yield: 10 cups.

Spirits for Sweets

For centuries, nogs and punches have spiced up holiday gatherings. The Brandied Apricot Nog and Chocolate Irish-Cream Punch are delicious, traditional beverages that you can serve with confidence.

But, for a spirited alternative, pair each serving of a liqueur-flavored dessert with a cordial glass of the same liqueur you used to make the dessert. The subtle flavors of Grand Marnier Mousse in Puff-Pastry Ring, for example, are enhanced by a sip of the orange-flavored liqueur.

And, of course, there's always champagne, a favorite for any festivity. Balance a sugary dessert with a "brut" champagne, which is dry, or team a tart dessert with a "sec" or "demi-sec" champagne, which is sweeter.

A symbol of celebration, champagne's convivial cachet was perhaps best described by Dom Pérignon, the Benedictine monk who presumably invented the bubbly beverage. Upon tasting his effervescent blend, the venerable monk is said to have exclaimed, "I am sipping stars!"

Treat Yourself to a Christmas Workshop

Looking for a way to put the "merry" back into your Christmas? Treat yourself to a holiday workshop! Your local craft shops, fabric stores, community centers, and garden centers are likely locales for inspiring workshops like those offered by The Herbfarm in Fall City, Washington.

Carrie Van Dyck, part owner and manager of The Herbfarm, will tell you the farm is at its peak during the summer. That's when the herb gardens—located in Snoqualmie Valley, near Seattle—are green and thriving. But The Herbfarm hums even in December, when its country store, restaurant, and mail-order house are a-buzz with holiday bustle. (For The Herbfarm's mail-order catalog, see the source listing on page 154.)

The spirit is perhaps most infectious at the farm's heart—the cluster of cozy greenhouses that often double as classrooms for a wide variety of workshops, including the two featured here.

Below right: In André Burman's wreath-making workshop, each participant composes evergreen bundles to create a wreath that will remain fresh and fragrant all season long.

Below: Oakmoss, a common lichen, and pine resin are just two of the ingredients used in EagleSong Randalls's potpourri-making workshop, shown on pages 122-23.

Wreaths Made Easy

When gardener and instructor André Burman leads one of his workshops on making evergreen wreaths, each student brings only wire cutters, garden gloves, and clippers. The Herbfarm and André provide the rest.

André begins by discussing which of the abundant Pacific Northwest evergreens work best and why. Because the needles of Fraser fir and Sitka spruce are green on one side and blue on the other, they provide variety of color. Cedar adds fragrance, and holly, whether variegated or traditional, contributes a visual emblem of Christmas. Even Scotch broom, usually considered a pest plant in the Northwest, has something to offer: Its deep green color and angular lines give pleasing contrasts.

Next André demonstrates his favorite method for making a wreath. He gathers different evergreens into a bundle and tightly wraps florist's wire around the bundle's base, which is about the size of a half

Above: Surrounded by boughs and baskets of fragrant evergreens, André demonstrates how to attach a bundle of greenery to a wire wreath back.

Above: In the greenhouse where André holds his wreath-making workshop, students make their own wreaths with the bows dangling from the rafters and the cedar, Fraser fir, and other evergreens found in twisted-twig baskets.

dollar. Then he wires the bundle's base to a metal, double-ring wreath back. André wires on more bundles, positioning the foliage to cover the base of the previous bundle, until the wreath is lush and full. He stabilizes the bundles by wrapping florist's wire in a spiral fashion around the circumference of the wreath and, as a finishing touch, wires on a bright ribbon bow or several pinecones.

In any workshop, the instructor's tips alone are sometimes worth the price of admission. As the students work on their wreaths, André passes on some advice of his own: Always make your bundles a little fuller than desired, as the evergreens will shrink a bit as they dry. And, to remove sap from your hands, rub butter into the sticky area before washing your hands—the sap will rinse right off.

Potpourri with a Purpose

Through her own company, the Moon Valley Herb Company, and the classes she teaches at The Herbfarm, folk-herbalist EagleSong Randalls passes on her unique vision of how the simplest of pursuits can resonate with meaning.

EagleSong's rejuvenating perspective is wonderfully at work when she conducts her workshop on making Northwest Holiday Potpourri. (For EagleSong's recipe, see the box on the opposite page.) Each ingredient has a history and a purpose. EagleSong uses kinnikinnick for its small, perfect leaf and also for its value among native peoples,

who believed that, when burned, it would carry prayers to the Great Mystery. The white pearly everlasting, harvested in June, is regarded by EagleSong and her children as tiny snowballs for the winter potpourri. "Since we harvest it in the season of greatest light," explains EagleSong, "we think of it as tiny lights to brighten the dark winter days."

Significance is also attached to the ingredients for the fixative. The three resins—frankincense, myrrh, and pine resin—represent the life blood of the forest and have been burned for centuries to create sacred spaces. Oakmoss is a lichen that absorbs scent and also serves to brighten the potpourri, as snow brightens the dark evergreens in winter.

Once mixed together and cured, Northwest Holiday Potpourri seems to release something even more eloquent than its glorious fragrance. As EagleSong says, simply, "This potpourri is a celebration of Light, which is the essence of every winter holiday. It is the time of rejoicing in the return of the Light."

Right: In her workshop on making Northwest Holiday Potpourri, EagleSong tells the story of each ingredient as she adds it to the mixture. The result: an exquisitely woodsy potpourri whose sum is much greater than its parts.

Northwest Holiday Potpourri

10 cups cedar tips
2 cups kinnikinnick (*uva-ursi*) (or
    substitute bay leaves)
2 cups pearly everlasting
1 cup oakmoss
1-2 cups red globe amaranth
Fixative (recipe follows)

Combine cedar tips and next 4 ingredients in a large bowl. Stir in fixative.

To cure, place mixture in a covered glass container for 4-6 weeks, stirring mixture once a week. If desired, adjust scent by adding more oil or other fixative ingredient.

For gifting, package potpourri in glass jars or cellophane envelopes.

Fixative:

¼ cup frankincense
¼ cup myrrh
¼ cup pine resin
1 cup Ceylon cinnamon
¼ cup orrisroot, cut up
Northwest Forest Oil

Using a mortar and pestle or similar tools, crush frankincense and next 2 ingredients into small particles. Repeat to crush cinnamon into ½" bits. Combine ingredients in a medium bowl. Add orrisroot and about 35 drops of oil; mix well.

Note: For potpourri ingredients, see the source listing on page 154.

Above: Two dolls in the nursery of the Stettheimer House delight in their own Christmas tree. In a frieze near the ceiling, Noah's Ark figures parade the room in 1920s-style beach clothes.

The Smallest Christmas Ever

Many Christmas mornings, young eyes have lit up at the sight of a dollhouse filled with miniature treasures. Dollhouses, delightful playthings for young and old, have a rich history.

The earliest dollhouses were made in western Europe for the nobility and wealthy middle-class adults of the 17th century. Because of their charming make-believe quality, dollhouses eventually became favorite toys for children, too.

The Museum of the City of New York, dedicated to urban history and culture, has collected toys since it was founded in 1923. The toy collection is most noted for its superb collection of dolls and dollhouses. The year-round exhibit features 11 tiny houses, all contributed (and at one time played with) by New York families. Two houses in the collection celebrate the Christmas season with garlands, ornaments, and fully decorated trees.

Altadena's House, donated to the museum in 1951, is decorated annually with five-inch-tall Christmas trees, surrounded by teensy presents, in the sitting room and nursery. The house was given to the museum with an unusual added benefit—maintenance. For more than 30 years, the donor, Betty Whitman, would come to the museum and clean the tiny house every six months with silver

polish and little mops and dusters. It was a labor of love and respect. Built in 1895, this house was a gift to Betty's mother, Altadena, from Altadena's father.

In another miniature structure, the high style of Art Deco can be seen. In the 1920s, New Yorker Carrie Stettheimer exercised her creative talents by designing and constructing an exquisite dollhouse. The Stettheimers were aristocratic and artistic, and Carrie managed the family household while her sisters blazed trails in literature and art. Her dollhouse

Above: Two dolls original to Altadena's House, a child and baby, occupy the nursery. Altadena's furrier made the ermine rug.

Left: On the first floor of Altadena's House, the sitting room was furnished to miniature scale, one inch to a foot. A jeweler made the chandelier. Betty Whitman needlepointed the rug when she and her mother, Altadena, refurbished the dollhouse.

Right: Carrie Stettheimer proved to be a master of collage. Her decorative style was sophisticated, but fun. The house has, among other furnishings, postage-stamp-size original works of art and an elevator.

is furnished with tiny original works of art contributed by famous artists and sculptors who were friends of the family, such as William Zorach, Gaston Lachaise, Claggett Wilson, and Marcel Duchamp.

At the family's request, in 1971, curator John Noble restored Carrie's dollhouse and decorated it for a Christmas party. He made foil Christmas trees in an elegant manner befitting the house. He also constructed numerous stylish dolls—likenesses of the three Stettheimer sisters and their renowned friends—from cotton, plaster, and wire. With an appreciation for artistic flair that Carrie would have approved, John based the Christmas decorations on the family's own holiday style, which included crafting jeweled trees and draping windows with the latest "modern" invention—cellophane.

In these two miniature houses, all dolled up for the holidays, a small world comes to life with the promise of Christmas, and the fascination with a land of miniatures lives on.

Gifts That Pamper And Please

Fill a basket with these herbal temptations for a gift that will transform an everyday routine into a luxury. For information on ordering the oils used in these recipes, see the source listing on page 154.

Left: Light as a whisper, dusting powder glides on like silk and releases a subtle perfume. To make the Lavender-Rose Powder, blend one cup each of talc and cornstarch with 1/8 teaspoon each of lavender and cinnamon oil and 10 drops of rose oil. Let the mixture dry on waxed paper.

Right: When presented with your handwritten labels, these herbal concoctions make thoughtful gifts. From after-shaves to bath salts, powders, and oils, these luxuries will please everyone on your list. There's even a bath treat that kids will love: To prepare the Almond Bubble Bath, simply add 1/2 cup of grated, unscented soap to the Almond Milk Bath (above right).

Lavender-Rose Bath Salts

1 cup Epsom salts
1/2 cup borax
12 drops each lavender and rose oil
lavender paste food coloring

Position knife blade in food processor bowl; add salts and borax. Top with cover and process until well blended. In a separate bowl, add oils. Dip tip of toothpick into paste and dot into oil. Repeat until oil is pale in color; add to dry ingredients. Dry mixture on waxed paper before packaging. Use 1/2 cup per bath.

Almond Milk Bath

1/3 cup powdered milk
1 tablespoon (1 package) unflavored gelatin, dry
1 cup Epsom salts
1/3 cup borax
1 teaspoon almond extract
pink paste food coloring

Position knife blade in food processor bowl; add powered milk, gelatin, salts, and borax. Top with cover and process until well blended. In a separate bowl, add extract. Follow above instructions for coloring, drying, and packaging.

Above: Bags of delicate lace release relaxing chamomile and skin-softening oatmeal. Hang one or two bags from the faucet and let warm water flow through them as the tub fills.

Above: These scented Bubbling Bath Oils provide a relaxing bath and help to hydrate dry winter skin. Fill small jars with one tablespoon of glycerin, five drops of liquid soap, and, depending on the scent you want, one tablespoon of either almond extract, lemon oil, or rose oil. Pour the entire bottle into running water for a bath filled with fragrance and froth.

Oatmeal-Chamomile Bath Bags

4 chamomile tea bags
3½ cups oatmeal
1 cup bran
4 tablespoons borax
3 tablespoons grated, unscented soap

Open tea bags and empty tea into a small bowl; discard bags. Set aside. Position knife blade in food processor bowl. Add oatmeal and bran. Top with cover and process until fine. Add borax, grated soap, and tea. Fill lace bags (see below) with ¼ cup of mixture. Tie bag closed with a length of colorfast satin ribbon or a doubled strand of embroidery floss.

Lace Bags

Note: All seam allowances are ¼".
For 1 lace bag, cut 1 (3" x 10") rectangle from lace. Fold ends under and stitch a narrow hem in each. With right sides facing, fold lace in half to make a 3" x 5" rectangle. Stitch long side edges together. Turn and fill lace bag with ¼ cup of the oatmeal-chamomile mixture.

Right: Whether smoothed on with cotton or mixed with cool water and splashed on, the Lavender Facial Refresher is delightfully invigorating to both men and women. Men will also relish the spicy scents and energizing qualities of the Menthol and Woodland after-shaves.

Lavender Facial Refresher

1 (14-ounce) bottle of witch hazel
handful lavender sprigs

Place lavender sprigs in bottle of witch hazel. Let steep for 2 weeks. Strain witch hazel into a clean bottle, discarding lavender sprigs.

Menthol After-shave

1 tablespoon witch hazel
1 tablespoon menthol alcohol
pinch of alum
¼ teaspoon boric acid
1 teaspoon glycerin
¼ cup distilled water

Mix witch hazel and alcohol in a small bowl. Set aside. Heat alum, boric acid, and glycerin in distilled water in microwave until dissolved (about 1½ minutes on HIGH). Let cool; combine mixtures in decorative jar and seal.
For Woodland After-shave, substitute rubbing alcohol for menthol alcohol. Add 5 drops woodland oil after the 2 mixtures are combined.

Patterns

LARGE LEAF
For tablecloth, cut 32 from assorted prints.

SMALL LEAF
For napkins, cut 4 from assorted prints.

Holiday Leaf Tablecloth and Napkins

**Instructions are on page 5.
Patterns are full-size.**

Wooden Stars

**Instructions are on page 45.
Pattern is full-size.**

**Holiday Leaf Tablecloth
Placement Diagram**
Note: Repeat pattern around all 4 sides of tablecloth.

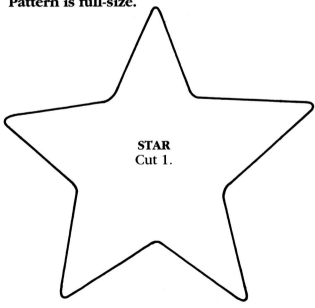

STAR
Cut 1.

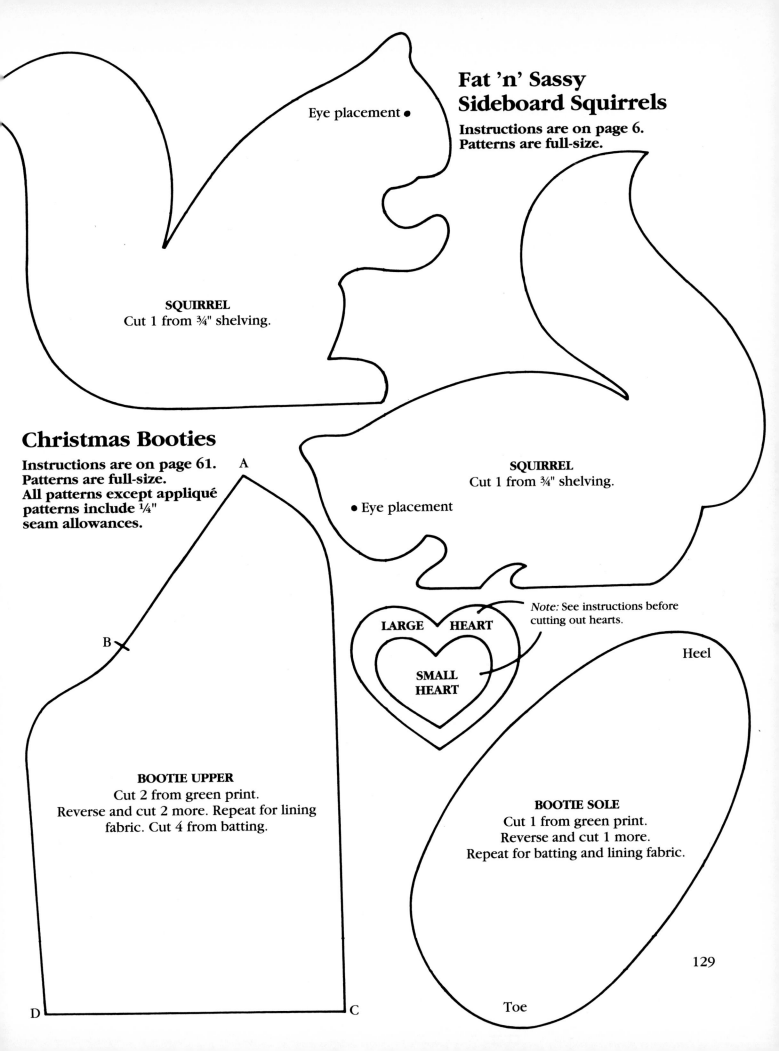

Eye placement ●

Fat 'n' Sassy
Sideboard Squirrels

Instructions are on page 6.
Patterns are full-size.

SQUIRREL
Cut 1 from ¾" shelving.

SQUIRREL
Cut 1 from ¾" shelving.

● Eye placement

Christmas Booties

Instructions are on page 61.
Patterns are full-size.
All patterns except appliqué
patterns include ¼"
seam allowances.

A

B

Note: See instructions before
cutting out hearts.

LARGE HEART

SMALL HEART

Heel

BOOTIE UPPER
Cut 2 from green print.
Reverse and cut 2 more. Repeat for lining
fabric. Cut 4 from batting.

BOOTIE SOLE
Cut 1 from green print.
Reverse and cut 1 more.
Repeat for batting and lining fabric.

129

D   C

Toe

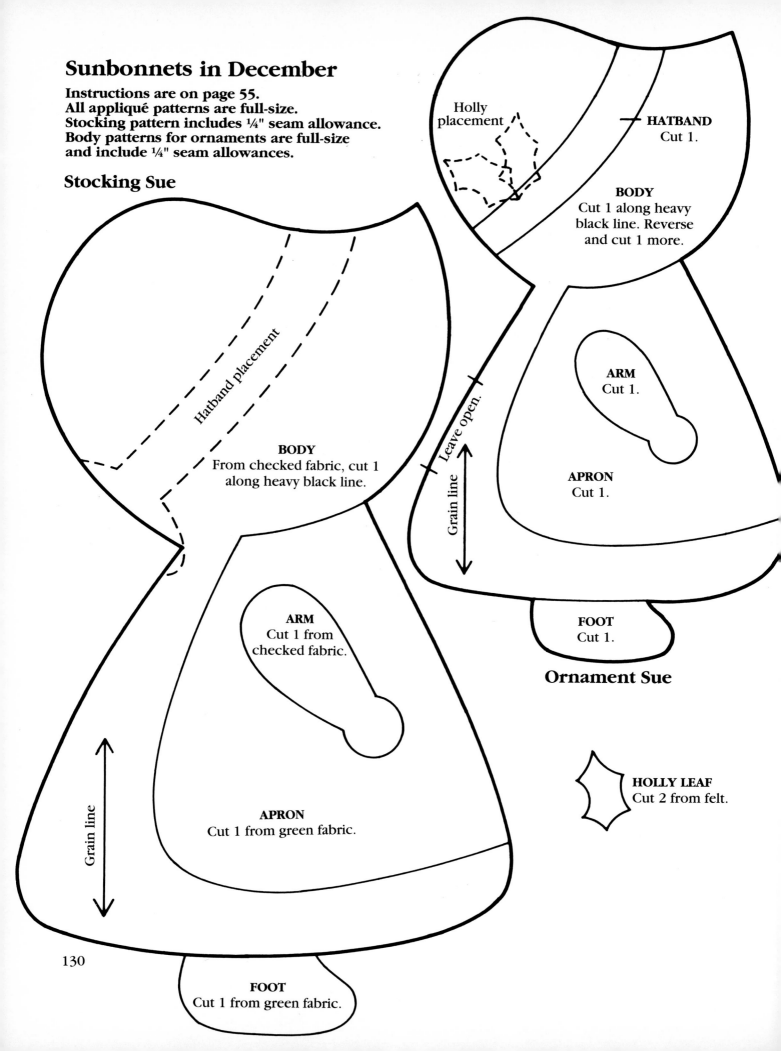

Sunbonnets in December

Instructions are on page 55.
All appliqué patterns are full-size.
Stocking pattern includes ¼" seam allowance.
Body patterns for ornaments are full-size
and include ¼" seam allowances.

Stocking Sue

Holly placement

HATBAND
Cut 1.

BODY
Cut 1 along heavy black line. Reverse and cut 1 more.

Hatband placement

BODY
From checked fabric, cut 1 along heavy black line.

Leave open.

Grain line

ARM
Cut 1.

APRON
Cut 1.

ARM
Cut 1 from checked fabric.

FOOT
Cut 1.

Ornament Sue

Grain line

APRON
Cut 1 from green fabric.

HOLLY LEAF
Cut 2 from felt.

FOOT
Cut 1 from green fabric.

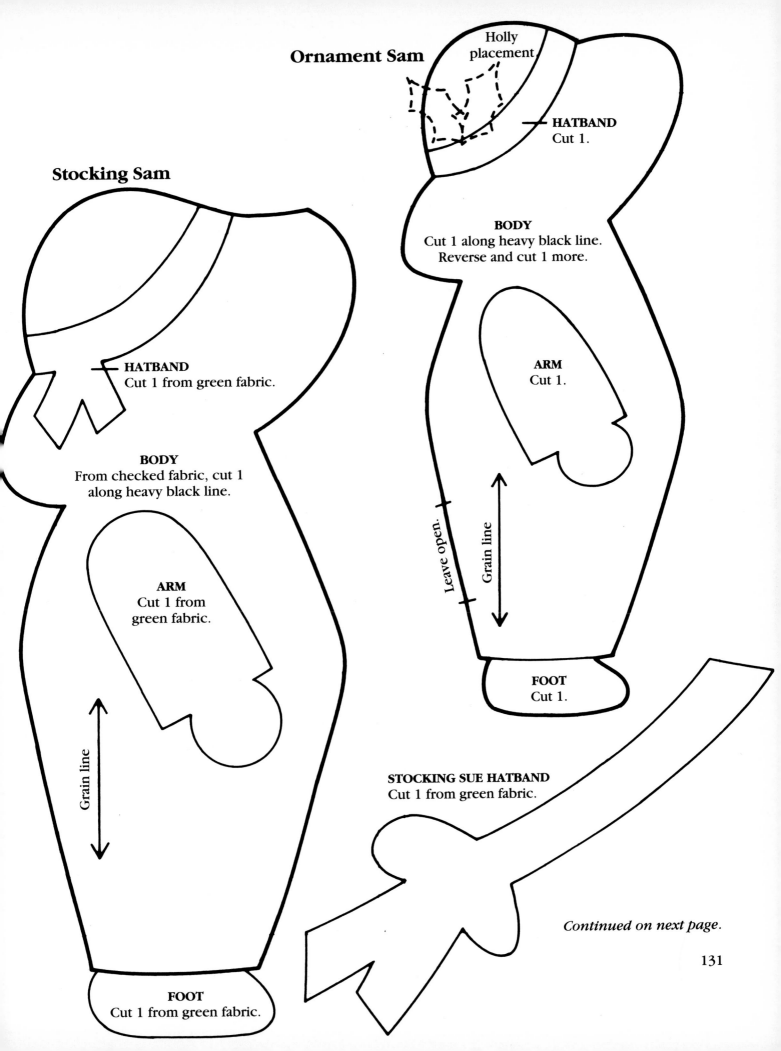

Ornament Sam

Holly placement

HATBAND
Cut 1.

BODY
Cut 1 along heavy black line.
Reverse and cut 1 more.

ARM
Cut 1.

Leave open.

Grain line

FOOT
Cut 1.

Stocking Sam

HATBAND
Cut 1 from green fabric.

BODY
From checked fabric, cut 1
along heavy black line.

ARM
Cut 1 from
green fabric.

Grain line

FOOT
Cut 1 from green fabric.

STOCKING SUE HATBAND
Cut 1 from green fabric.

Continued on next page.

131

Extend stocking ¾".
Extend lining 5½".

Each square = 1".

SUNBONNET SUE AND SAM STOCKING
Cut 1 from red pindot. Reverse and cut 1 more.
Repeat for lining fabric.

Apple Tree Skirt

Instructions begin on page 59.
Patterns are full-size.

Note: Patterns are for machine-appliqué. If you wish to appliqué by hand, add ¼" seam allowance to pattern pieces.

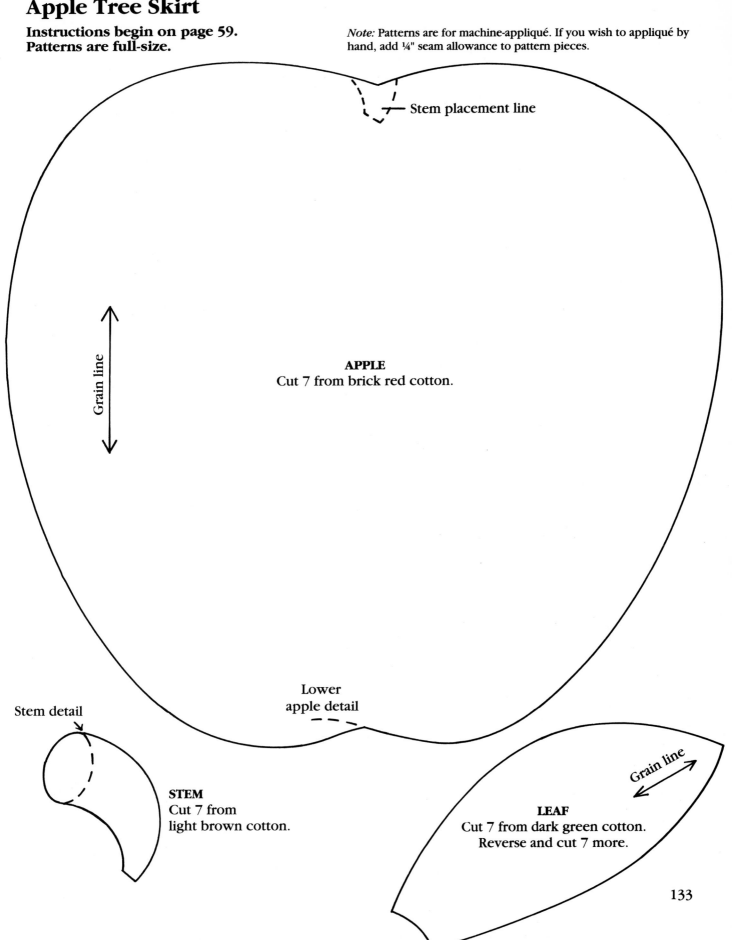

Stem placement line

Grain line

APPLE
Cut 7 from brick red cotton.

Lower
apple detail

Stem detail

STEM
Cut 7 from
light brown cotton.

Grain line

LEAF
Cut 7 from dark green cotton.
Reverse and cut 7 more.

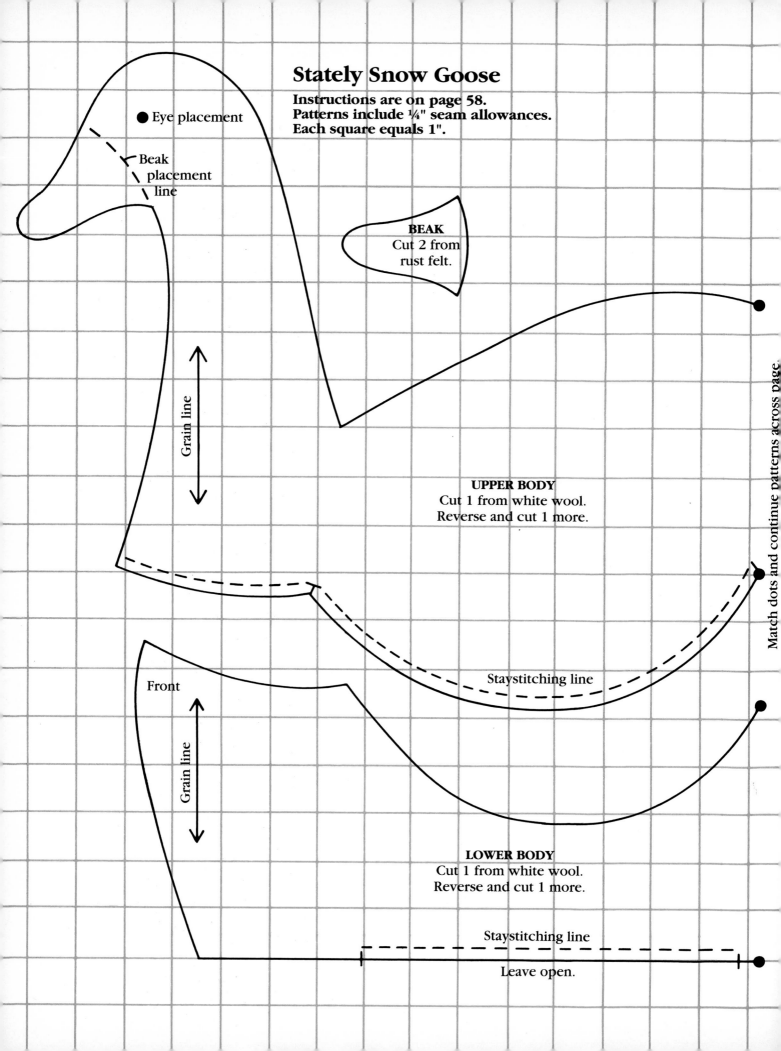

Stately Snow Goose

Instructions are on page 58.
Patterns include ¼" seam allowances.
Each square equals 1".

● Eye placement

Beak placement line

BEAK
Cut 2 from rust felt.

Grain line

UPPER BODY
Cut 1 from white wool.
Reverse and cut 1 more.

Match dots and continue patterns across page.

Staystitching line

Front

Grain line

LOWER BODY
Cut 1 from white wool.
Reverse and cut 1 more.

Staystitching line

Leave open.

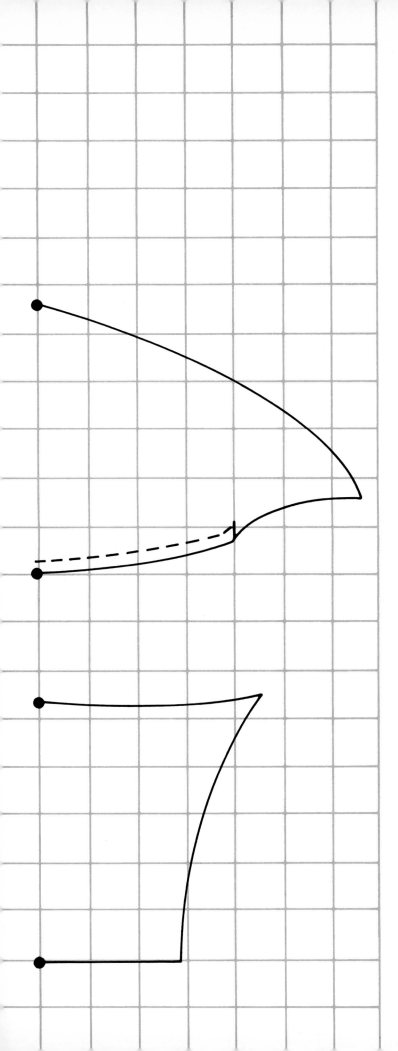

Perforated-Paper Stars

Instructions are on page 45.

Design 1

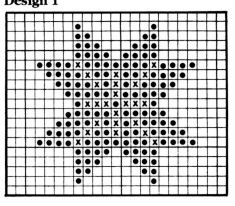

Design 2

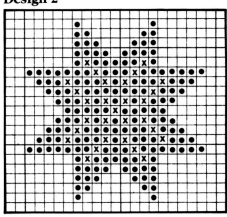

Design 3

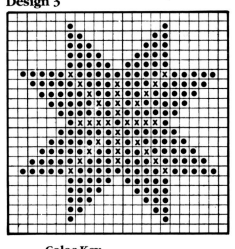

Color Key

•	725 Lt. Topaz *or*
•	783 Med. Topaz *or*
•	796 Royal Blue
x	145GS1 Gold Metallic Beads (use with DMC 725 and 796) *or* 140 Sapphire Beads (use with DMC 783).

Note: Numbers are for DMC floss and Westrim Crafts Beads.

Celestial Cheer for All the Year

Instructions begin on page 43.

Instructions begin on page 43.

Chart for Sun

Note: Follow chart to stitch both cross-stitch ornament and needlepoint pillow.

Color Key for Cross-Stitch

·		Ecru
♥	347	Red
o	353	Pink
−	725	Lt. Topaz
x	783	Med. Topaz
●	781	Dk. Topaz
□	796	Royal Blue
◣	869	Med. Brown
■	3031	Dk. Brown

/	353 Pink (1 strand) + 725 Lt. Topaz (2 strands)
u	781 Dk. Topaz (1 strand) + 783 Med. Topaz (2 strands)
✓	783 Med. Topaz (1 strand) + 725 Lt. Topaz (2 strands)

Note: Numbers are for DMC embroidery floss. Cross-stitch, using 3 strands of floss.

Color Key for Needlepoint

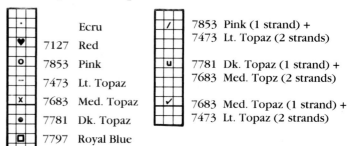

·		Ecru
♥	7127	Red
o	7853	Pink
−	7473	Lt. Topaz
x	7683	Med. Topaz
●	7781	Dk. Topaz
□	7797	Royal Blue
◣	7499	Med. Brown
■	7526	Dk. Brown

/	7853 Pink (1 strand) + 7473 Lt. Topaz (2 strands)
u	7781 Dk. Topaz (1 strand) + 7683 Med. Topz (2 strands)
✓	7683 Med. Topaz (1 strand) + 7473 Lt. Topaz (2 strands)

Note: Numbers are for DMC Floralia Persian wool. Work basketweave stitch or continental stitch, using 3 strands of wool. Stitch background with 7797 Royal Blue until finished design size measures 12" x 12".

Chart for Moon

Note: Follow chart to stitch both cross-stitch ornament and needlepoint pillow.

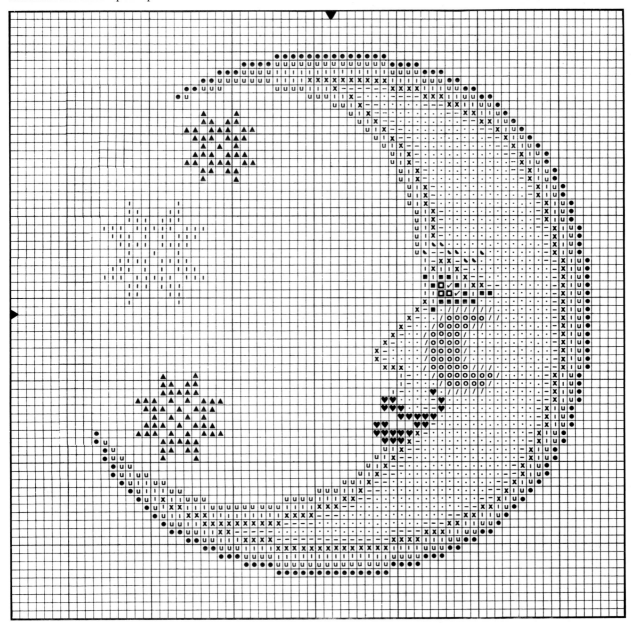

Color Key for Cross-Stitch

✓		Ecru
♥	347	Red
○	353	Pink
·	725	Lt. Topaz
▲	783	Med. Topaz
ı	781	Dk. Topaz
▢	796	Royal Blue
↘	869	Med. Brown
■	3031	Dk. Brown

/	353 Pink (1 strand) + 725 Lt. Topaz (2 strands)
●	783 Med. Topaz (1 strand) + 781 Dk. Topaz (2 strands)
u	781 Dk. Topaz (1 strand) + 783 Med. Topaz (2 strands)
x	725 Lt. Topaz (1 strand) + 783 Med. Topaz (2 strands)
–	783 Med. Topaz (1 strand) + 725 Lt. Topaz (2 strands)

Note: Numbers are for DMC embroidery floss. Cross-stitch, using 3 strands of floss.

Color Key for Needlepoint

✓		Ecru
♥	7127	Red
○	7853	Pink
·	7473	Lt. Topaz
▲	7683	Med. Topaz
ı	7781	Dk. Topaz
▢	7797	Royal Blue
↘	7499	Med. Brown
■	7526	Dk. Brown

/	7853 Pink (1 strand) + 7473 Lt. Topaz (2 strands)
●	7683 Med. Topaz (1 strand + 7781 Dk. Topaz (2 strands)
u	7781 Dk. Topaz (1 strand) + 7683 Med. Topaz (2 strands)
x	7473 Lt. Topaz (1 strand) + 7683 Med. Topaz (2 strands)
–	7683 Med. Topaz (1 strand) + 7473 Lt. Topaz (2 strands)

Note: Numbers are for DMC Floralia Persian wool. Work basketweave or continental stitch, using 3 strands of wool. Stitch background with 7797 Royal Blue until finished design size measures 12" x 12".

A Quintet of Appliqué Ornaments

Instructions are on page 35.
Patterns are full-size.

Note: Cut out each ornament base using pinking shears.
Cut out each appliqué piece using sewing scissors.

Color Key
1 Dark Turquoise
2 Black
3 Turquoise
4 Yellow
5 Lavender
6 Red
7 Green
8 Tan

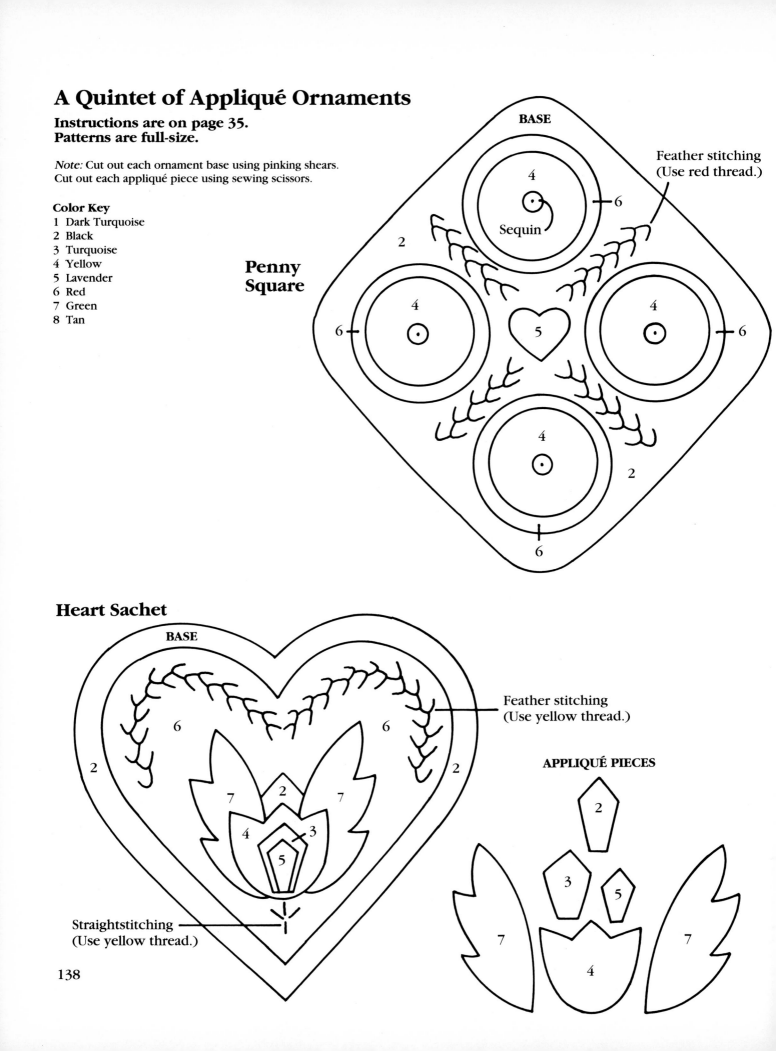

Penny Square

BASE

Sequin

Feather stitching
(Use red thread.)

Heart Sachet

BASE

Feather stitching
(Use yellow thread.)

APPLIQUÉ PIECES

Straightstitching
(Use yellow thread.)

138

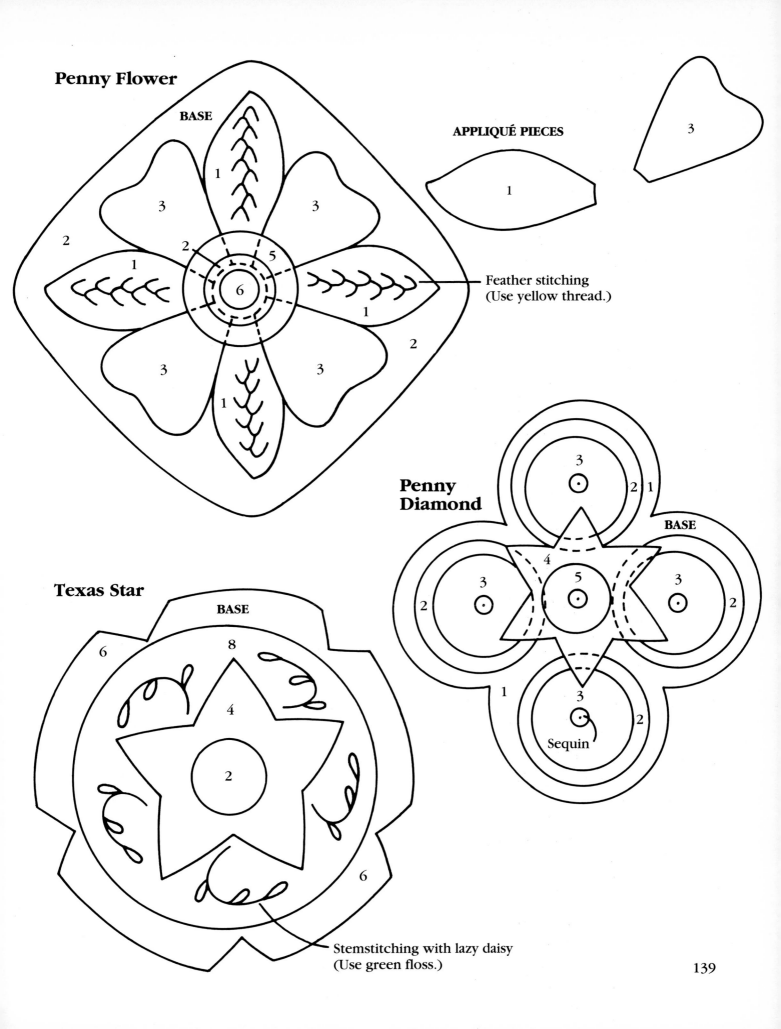

Penny Flower

BASE

APPLIQUÉ PIECES

Feather stitching
(Use yellow thread.)

Penny Diamond

BASE

Sequin

Texas Star

BASE

Stemstitching with lazy daisy
(Use green floss.)

Little House Chair Mat

Instructions begin on page 36.

For full-size pattern, enlarge pattern 118% on copy machine.

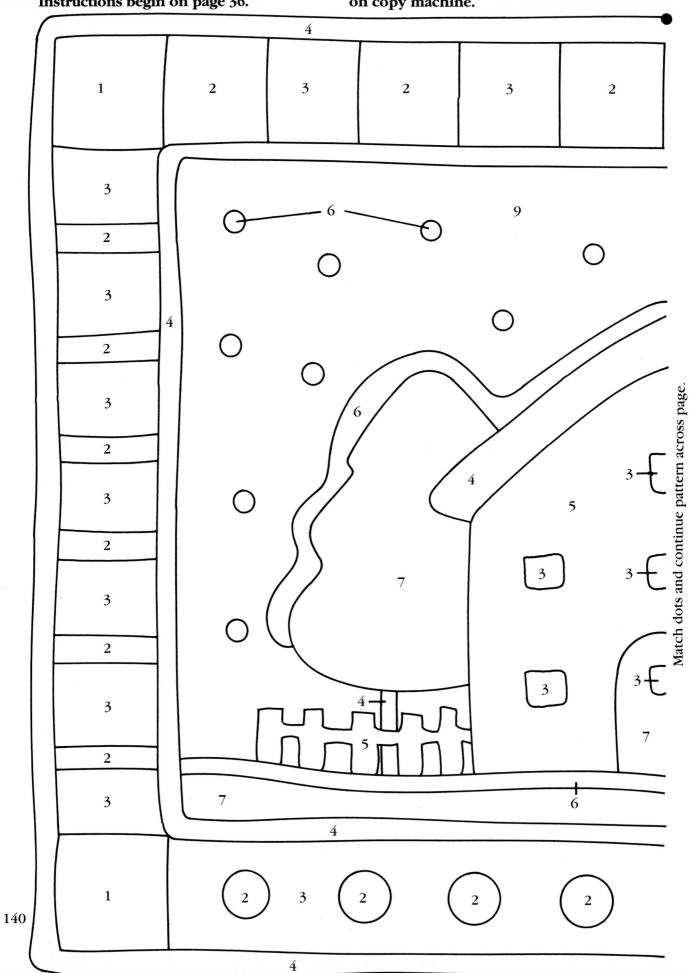

Match dots and continue pattern across page.

Note: Color Key is on page 142.

Snowflake placement
(Use cream wool.)

141

Little House Ornament

Instructions begin on page 36.
Pattern is full-size.

Color Key for Ornament
1 Red
2 Tan
3 Green
4 Brown
5 Cream
6 Light Blue
7 Medium Blue
8 Dark Blue

Snowflake placement
(Use cream wool.)

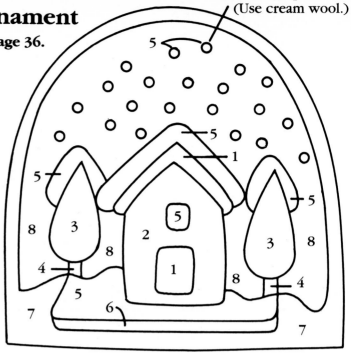

Playful Pairs

Instructions are on page 39.
Patterns are full-size.

Note: For Mittens Ornament on opposite page, cut out base using pinking shears. Cut out all other pieces using sewing scissors.

Bear-and-Heart Ornament

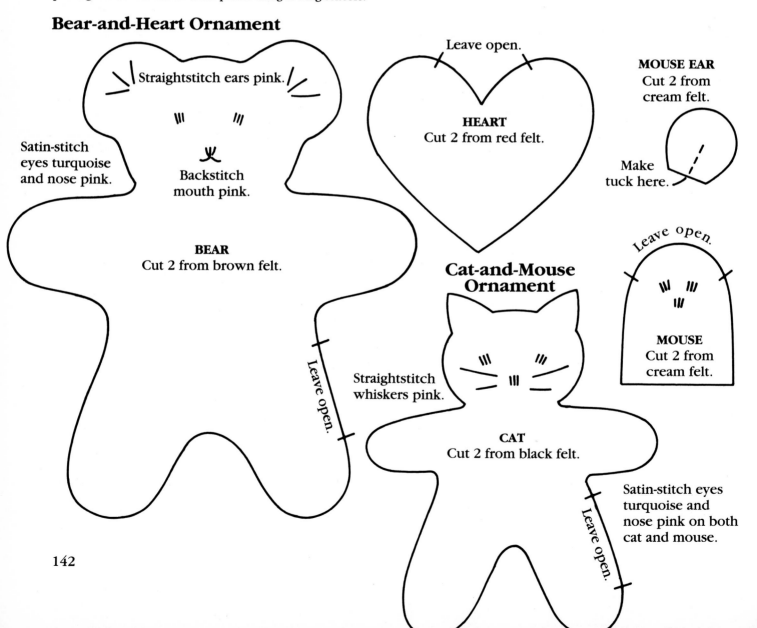

Straightstitch ears pink.

Satin-stitch eyes turquoise and nose pink.

Backstitch mouth pink.

BEAR
Cut 2 from brown felt.

Leave open.

HEART
Cut 2 from red felt.

MOUSE EAR
Cut 2 from cream felt.

Make tuck here.

Leave open.

Cat-and-Mouse Ornament

MOUSE
Cut 2 from cream felt.

Straightstitch whiskers pink.

CAT
Cut 2 from black felt.

Leave open.

Leave open.

Satin-stitch eyes turquoise and nose pink on both cat and mouse.

Painted Tin Angel

Instructions are on page 53.
Pattern is full-size.

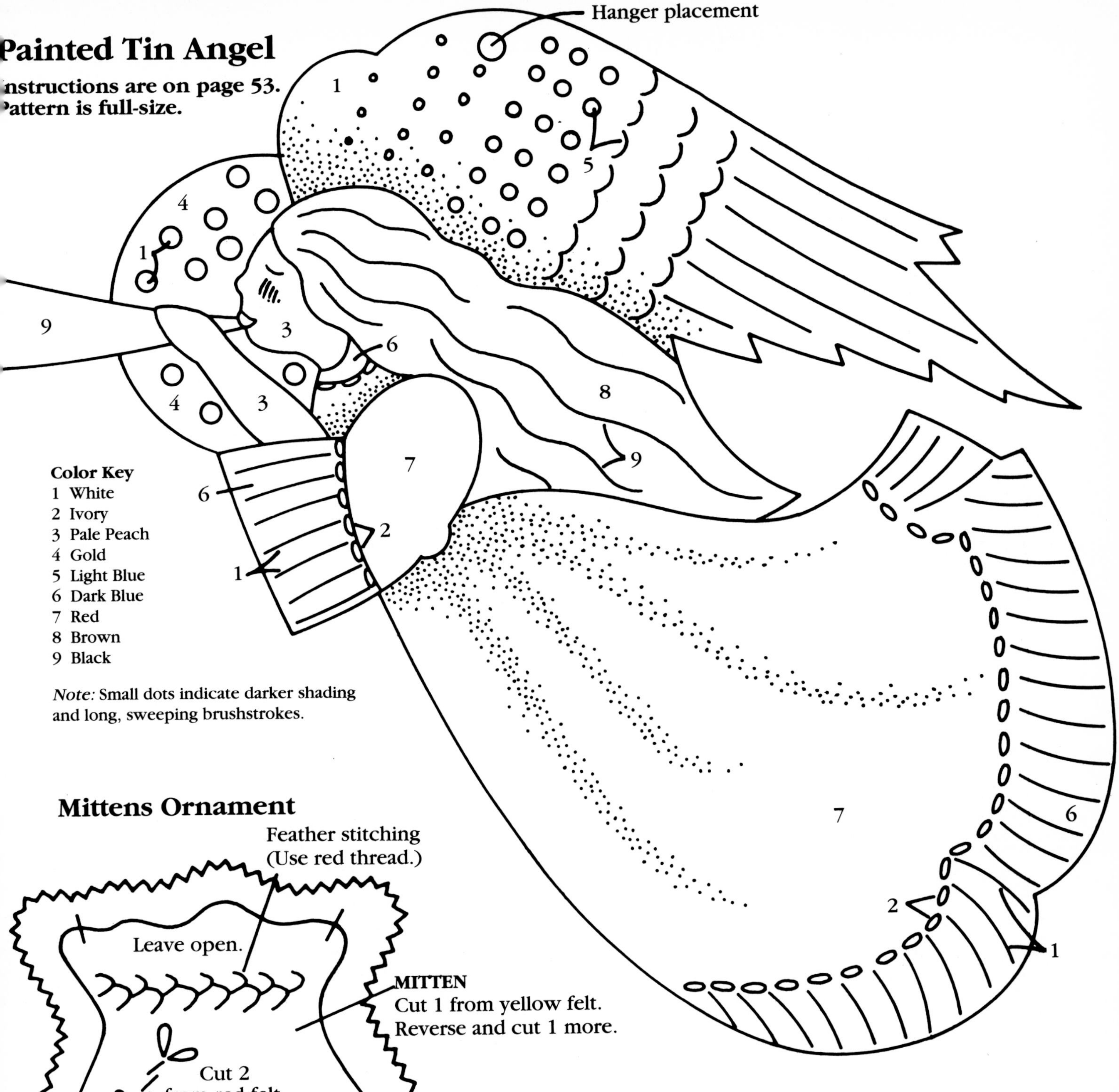

Hanger placement

Color Key
1 White
2 Ivory
3 Pale Peach
4 Gold
5 Light Blue
6 Dark Blue
7 Red
8 Brown
9 Black

Note: Small dots indicate darker shading and long, sweeping brushstrokes.

Mittens Ornament

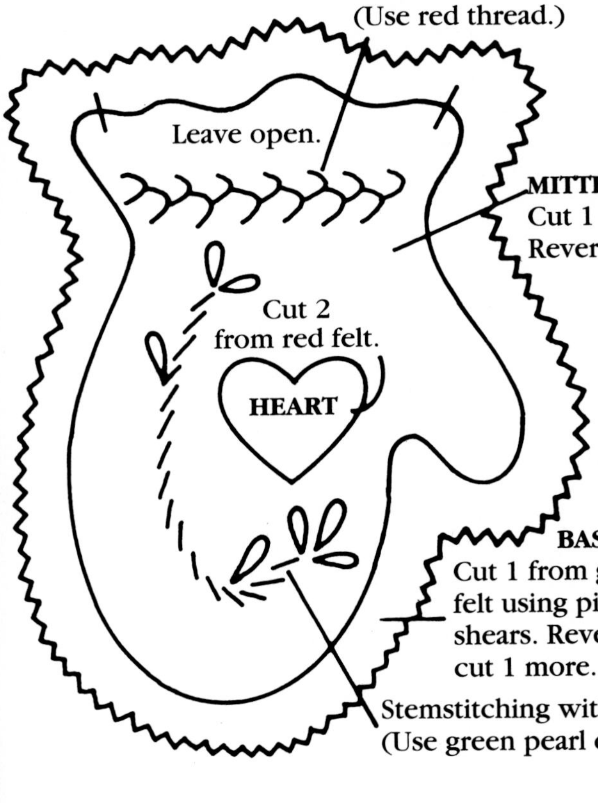

Feather stitching
(Use red thread.)

Leave open.

MITTEN
Cut 1 from yellow felt.
Reverse and cut 1 more.

Cut 2
from red felt.

HEART

BASE
Cut 1 from green
felt using pinking
shears. Reverse and
cut 1 more.

Stemstitching with lazy daisy
(Use green pearl cotton.)

Knitted Baby Stockings and Mittens

Instructions begin on page 68.

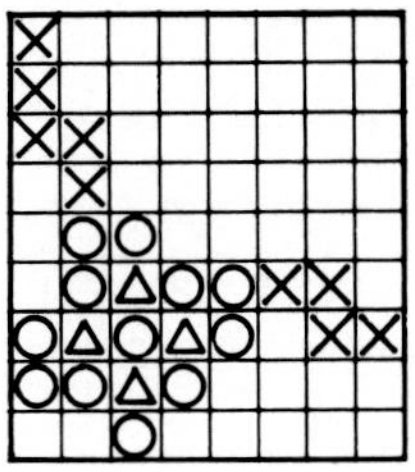

Chart for Flower
Note: Duplicate-stitch design, using 1 strand of pearl cotton. If desired, vary placement of leaves. Knitting Abbreviations are on page 153.

Color Key
⊠ Light Green
○ Pink
△ Yellow

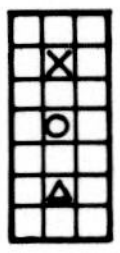

143

Flower-Top Box

**Instructions are on page 57.
Pattern is full-size.**

Note: Continue pattern at right edge, omitting tab, to make 4 panels as indicated in Placement Diagram.

TAB

Continue pattern here.

**FLOWER-TOP BOX
PLACEMENT DIAGRAM**

Petals

1 2 3 4

Tab

1 2 3 4

A B C D

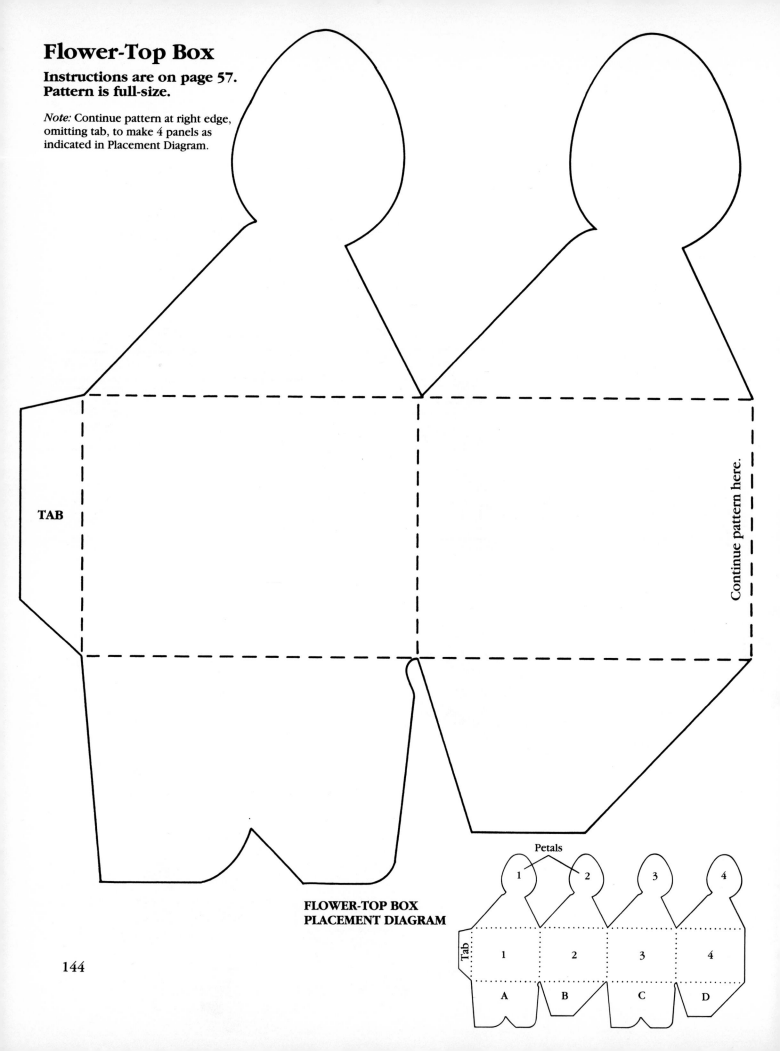

Heirloom Silhouettes

Instructions are on page 71.
Patterns are full-size.

Note: Cut out all white areas of design, beginning with inner areas first and working toward outer edges.

Penelope Bear

Instructions begin on page 69.
Patterns are full-size and include ¼" seam allowances.

Leave open.

Attach arms to body at dots.
• •

ARM
Cut 2. Reverse and cut 2 more.

Leave open.

BODY BACK
Cut 1.

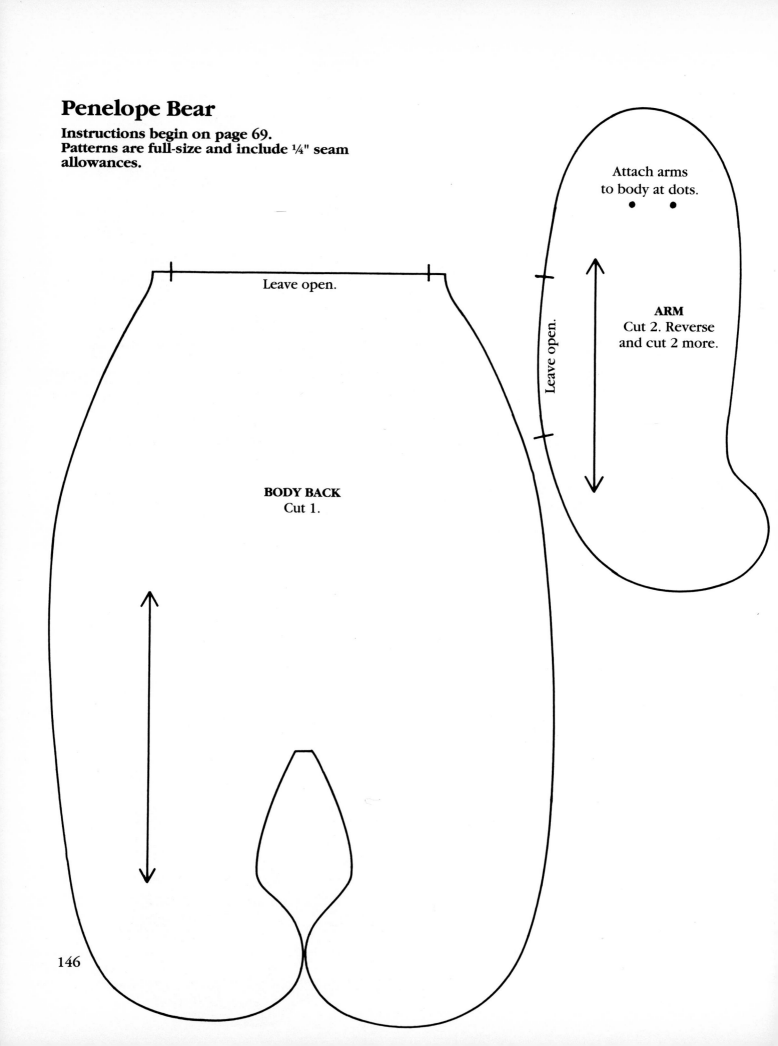

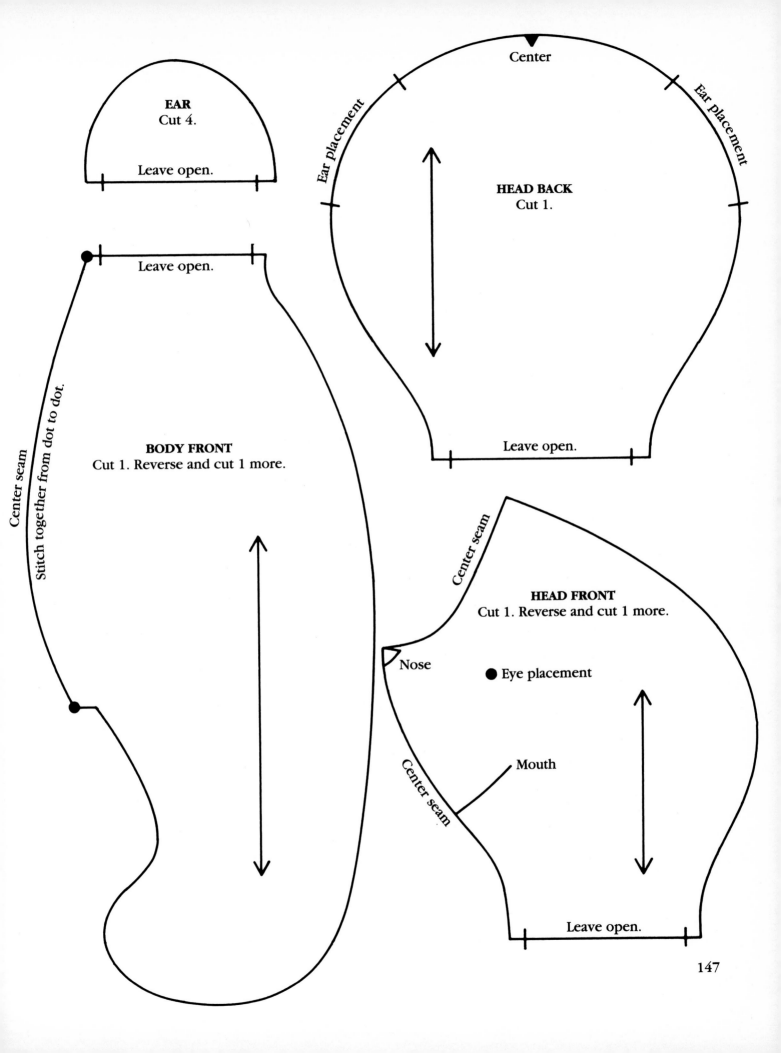

EAR
Cut 4.

Leave open.

Leave open.

Center

Ear placement

Ear placement

HEAD BACK
Cut 1.

Leave open.

Center seam

Stitch together from dot to dot.

BODY FRONT
Cut 1. Reverse and cut 1 more.

Center seam

HEAD FRONT
Cut 1. Reverse and cut 1 more.

Nose

● Eye placement

Center seam

Mouth

Leave open.

147

Cross-Stitch for the Kitchen

Instructions begin on page 86.

Note: Numbers are for DMC floss. Cross-stitch, using 2 strands of floss and stitching over 1 thread on Aida cloth and over 2 threads on Kali cloth. Use 2 strands of 501 Dk. Blue Green to backstitch stems and around leaves. Use 2 strands of 815 Med. Garnet to backstitch around cranberries. Use 2 strands of 3790 Dk. Beige Gray to backstitch borders around wreaths and sprigs.

Color Key

▲	815	Med. Garnet
○	335	Rose
◆	502	Blue Green
✳	503	Med. Blue Green
●	501	Dk. Blue Green
■	3790	Dk. Beige Gray

Chart for Hostess Apron Bib and Bread Cloth

Note: For bread cloth, omit backstitched borders.

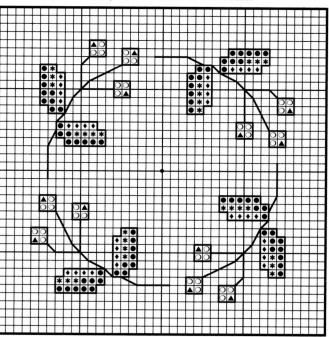

Chart for Hostess Apron Pocket

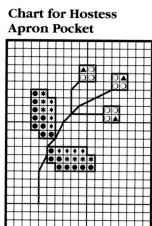

Letter Chart for Bread Cloth

Note: Cross-stitch, using 3 strands of 3790 Dk. Beige Gray. Use heavy black dot to center desired letter inside wreath.

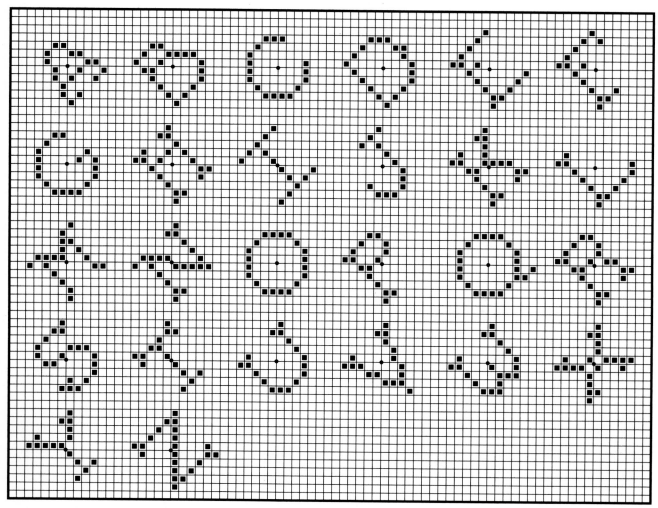

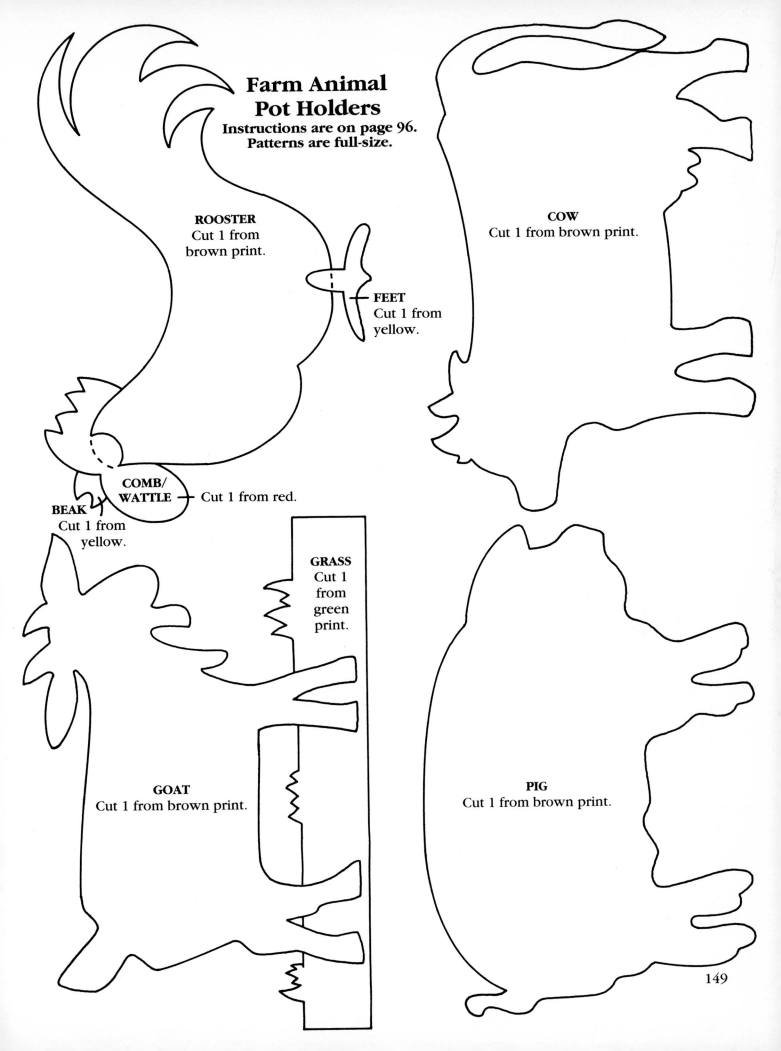

Farm Animal
Pot Holders
Instructions are on page 96.
Patterns are full-size.

ROOSTER
Cut 1 from
brown print.

FEET
Cut 1 from
yellow.

COW
Cut 1 from brown print.

COMB/
WATTLE — Cut 1 from red.

BEAK
Cut 1 from
yellow.

GRASS
Cut 1
from
green
print.

GOAT
Cut 1 from brown print.

PIG
Cut 1 from brown print.

149

A Snow-Frosted Village

Instructions begin on page 112.
Patterns are full-size.

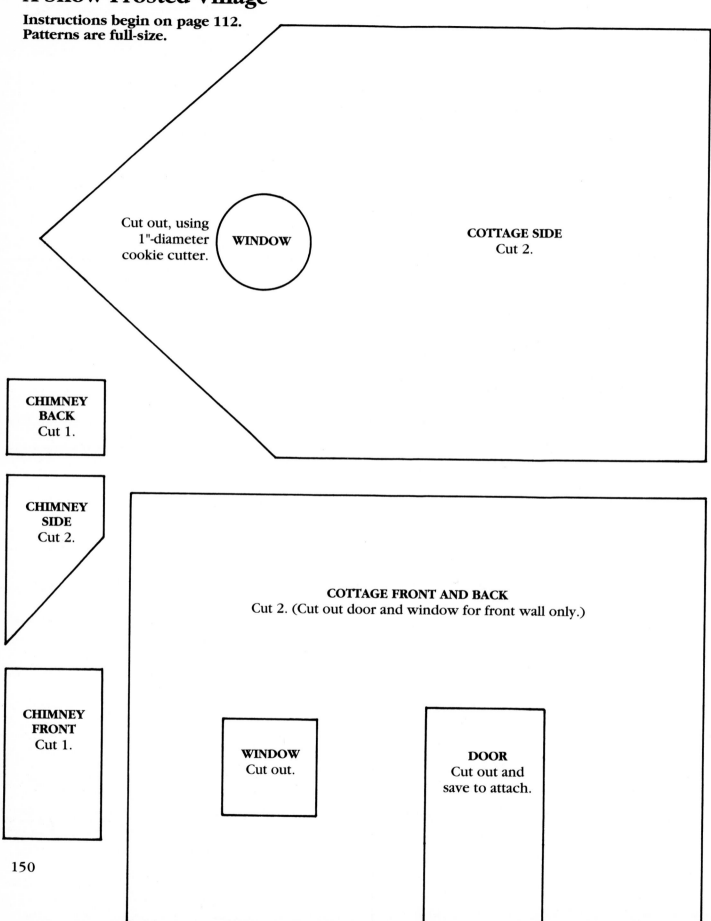

Cut out, using 1"-diameter cookie cutter.

WINDOW

COTTAGE SIDE
Cut 2.

CHIMNEY BACK
Cut 1.

CHIMNEY SIDE
Cut 2.

COTTAGE FRONT AND BACK
Cut 2. (Cut out door and window for front wall only.)

CHIMNEY FRONT
Cut 1.

WINDOW
Cut out.

DOOR
Cut out and save to attach.

150

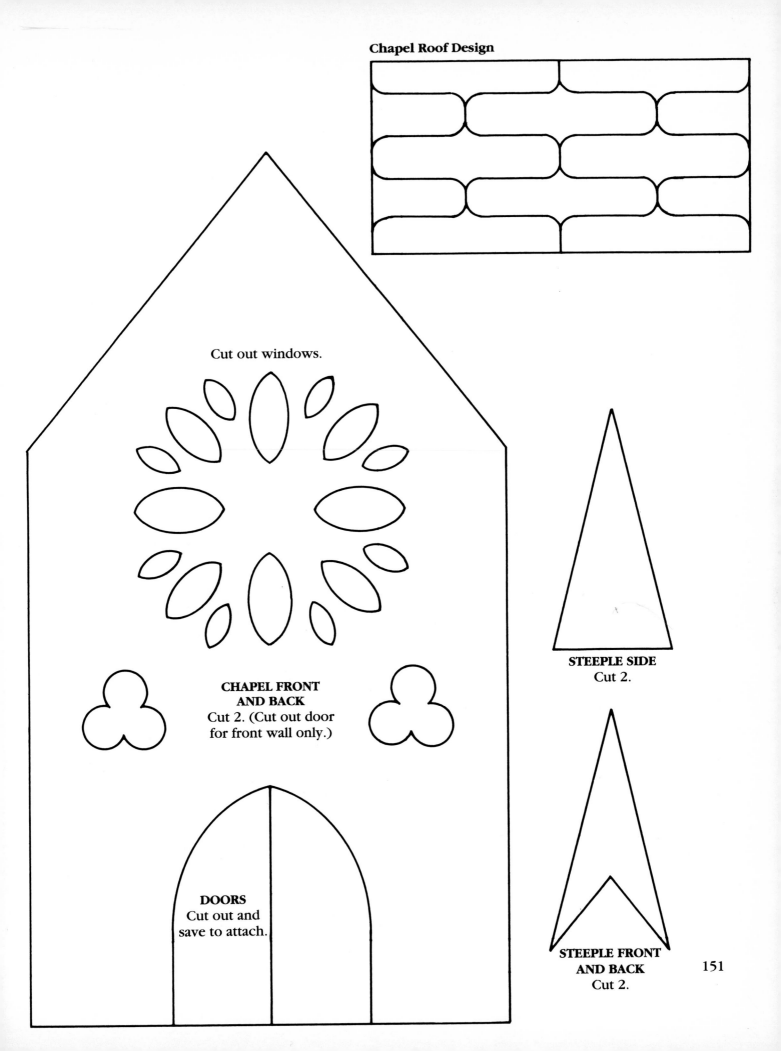

Chapel Roof Design

Cut out windows.

**CHAPEL FRONT
AND BACK**
Cut 2. (Cut out door
for front wall only.)

DOORS
Cut out and
save to attach.

STEEPLE SIDE
Cut 2.

**STEEPLE FRONT
AND BACK**
Cut 2.

151

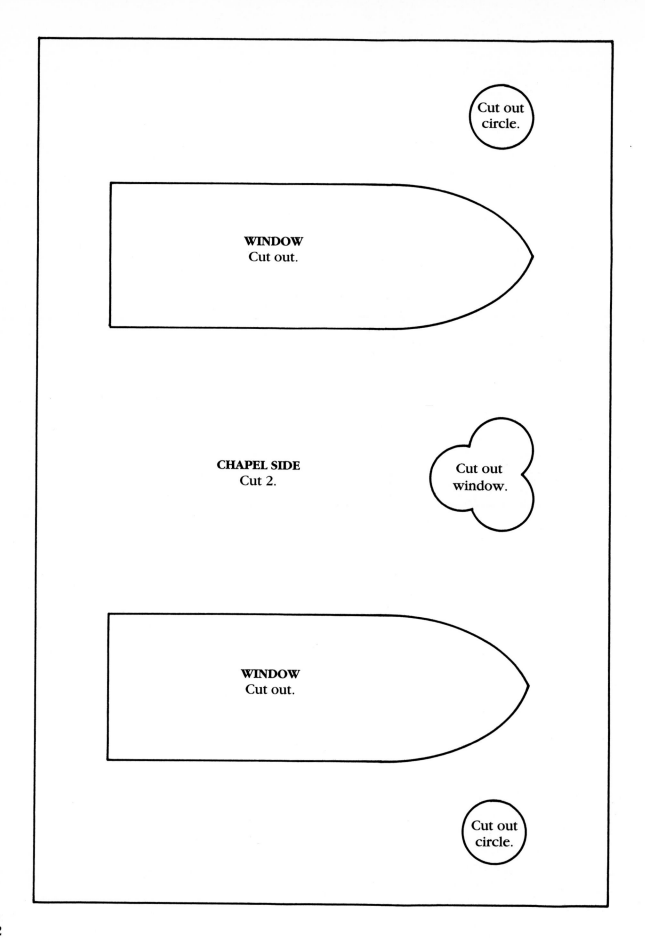

Cut out
circle.

WINDOW
Cut out.

CHAPEL SIDE
Cut 2.

Cut out
window.

WINDOW
Cut out.

Cut out
circle.

152

Santa-and-Me Photo Album

Instructions are on page 111.
Patterns are full-size. Circle pattern
includes ¼" seam allowance.

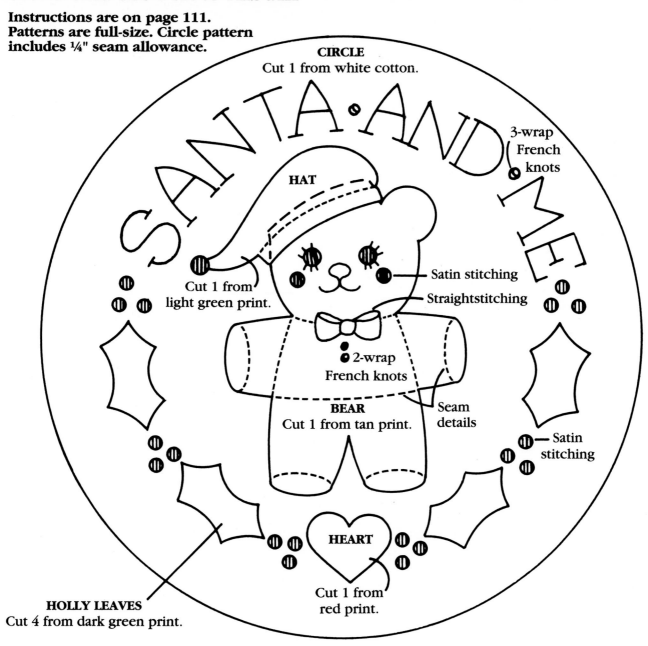

CIRCLE
Cut 1 from white cotton.

3-wrap
French
knots

HAT

Cut 1 from
light green print.

Satin stitching

Straightstitching

2-wrap
French knots

BEAR
Cut 1 from tan print.

Seam
details

Satin
stitching

HOLLY LEAVES
Cut 4 from dark green print.

HEART
Cut 1 from
red print.

Crochet Abbreviations

beg—begin(ning)
ch—chain(s)
dc—double crochet
lp(s)—loop(s)
rep—repeat
rnd(s)—round(s)
sc—single crochet
sk—skip
sl st—slip stitch
sp(s)—space(s)
st(s)—stitch(es)

Knitting Abbreviations

inc—increase
k—knit
p—purl
rem—remain(ing)
rep—repeat(ing)
rnd(s)—round(s)
sl—slip
st(s)—stitch(es)
St st—stockinette stitch (k 1 row, p 1 row)
tog—together

Contributors

Designers

Ginger Kean Berk, stockings and ornaments, 54.

Eleanore Brough, stitching of sun and moon pillows, 44.

Vicki D. Carter, painted gift boxes, 90.

Alice Cox, ribbon epaulets, 110.

Christine Davis, knitted stockings and mittens, 66.

Carol Cook Hagood, quilted booties, 61.

Charlotte Hagood, leaf figure, 8; leaf-print wrapping paper, 31; crocheted gift boxes, 47; crocheted stockings and mittens, 66; ornaments, 70; hair bows and barrettes, 108-10.

Brenda W. Kolb, napkins, 31.

Betsy Lardent, candle holder, napkin rings, 94; basket, 95.

Terri Lipman, tin angel, 53.

Denise Lohr, apron and bread cloth, 87.

Charlotte Lyons, appliqué ornaments, 34; hooked ornament and chair mat, 37; wool ornaments, 39.

Janet Miller, design work for sun and moon projects, 43-44; cross-stitch stars, 45.

Kathie Parker, bath salts, oils, powders, and after-shaves, 126-27.

Lou Souders, wool goose, 58; wool bear, 68.

St. Nicole Designs, tree skirt, 59.

Katie Stoddard, birdhouses, 52.

Karen Tindall Tillery, flat wraps, 78.

Carol M. Tipton, place cards, tablecloth, napkins, candlesticks, and napkin rings, 4; squirrels and garland, 6; candlesticks, 30; wooden stars, 45; silhouettes, 71; pot holders, 96.

Eileen Westfall, photo-album cover, 111.

Cyndi Wheeler, stitching of sun and moon ornaments, 43.

Julie A. Wilson, paste-paper gift boxes, 56.

Photographers

All photographs except for the following were taken by **John O'Hagan.**

Ralph Anderson, 7, 82, 85, 90, 101-2, 112, 119.

Ron Anderson, 114-15.

Gary Clark, 17, 21-25, 28, 76-77, 87-88, 94, 124-25.

Colleen Duffley, 18-20, 49-51, 74-75, 97, 99, 104-5, 116.

Mary-Gray Hunter, middle 16, lower left 26, 43.

Hal Lott, 72-73.

Beth Maynor, 10-14, bottom 15, upper 40, 41-42.

Melissa Springer, 29, upper 66.

Photostylists

All photographs except for the following were styled by **Katie Stoddard.**

Barbara Manning, 7.

Gloria Gale, 114-15.

Susan Merrill, 82, 85, 89, 90, 97, 99, 101, 102, 104-5, 112, 116, 119.

Joetta Moulden, 72-73.

Sources

★ Page 8—wool roving and craft supplies catalog: $2 to Stitcher's Market, P.O. Box 411, New Albany, OH 43054

★ Page 35—wool and rug hooking catalog: $4 to Braid-Aid, 466 Washington St., Pembroke, MA 02359

★ Page 42—redware pottery: Foltz Pottery, 225 N. Peartown Rd., Reinholds, PA 17569

★ Page 52—birdhouses: Walnut Hollow woodcraft products available at craft and department stores, or call 1-800-243-2089

★ Page 62—candle-decorating wax: HearthSong, Inc., P.O. Box B, Sebastopol, CA 95473

★ Pages 62-63—candle-making supplies: Pourette Mfg., P.O. Box 15220, Seattle, WA 98115

★ Page 115—Georgetown Christmas Market: Historic Georgetown, Inc., P.O. Box 667, George-town, CO 80444, or call 303-569-2840

★ Page 121—workshops and mail-order catalog: The Herbfarm, 32804 Issaquah-Fall City Rd., Fall City, WA 98024

★ Page 123—potpourri ingredients: $1.00 to Moon Valley Herb Co., P.O. Box 188, Snoqualmie, WA 98065

★ Page 126—scented oils: The Essential Oil Company, P.O. Box 206, Lake Oswego, OR 97034, or call 1-800-729-5912

Special thanks to:

Roslyn Oneille Hardy
Larry Hunter
Jennifer Mathews
Sidney Melton
Margaret Allen Northen
Bonnie Scaro
Richard D. Tucker
Rowena Wilson

Index

General

Recipes